SCIENCE ENQUIRY GAMES

(PUPILS AGED 11 - 14)

Active ways to learn and develop science enquiry skills

by Bob Ponchaud

and

Anne Goldsworthy

Educational Consultants Limited

First published in Great Britain by Millgate House Publishers 2010.

Millgate House Publishers is an imprint of
Millgate House Education Ltd
Unit 1, Zan Business Park
Crewe Road
Sandbach
CW11 4QD, UK
www.millgatehouse.co.uk

Edited by Brenda Keogh and Stuart Naylor

British Library Cataloguing in Publication Data
A record for this book is available from the British Library.

ISBN 9780-95562607-4

EAN 9780 955 62607 4

Typesetting, Graphic Design and PDF by Kathryn Stawpert
Illustrations by Ged Mitchell

Printed and bound in Great Britain by Crewe Colour Printers

Acknowledgments

There are several groups of people who have had an impact on this publication through their willingness to trial, and provide feedback on, our ideas and resources.

All the teachers and advisors who gave us invaluable help when developing the games.

Kathryn Stawpert who has expertly drawn all the materials together and turned them into a fun resource book and PDF.

Ged Mitchell who has skilfully turned ideas into images.

Jo Williams who has patiently managed the illustration process.

Finally the many teachers who, during INSET sessions, let caution to the wind and joined in enthusiastically with the games. We hope they, and their pupils, enjoy using the resources in this book.

Introduction

ENQUIRY AND GAMES

Scientific enquiry skills are vital to pupils' progress in science. Helping pupils to understand the nature of evidence is probably the most important thing we do in science education. By equipping them with the tools of scientific enquiry, we can really help pupils throughout school and in everyday life. Pupils who are able to use these skills effectively become competent and confident investigators. They also gain better appreciation of 'how science works' and in particular how scientific evidence can be properly used to help us understand and look after the world around us.

> "Helping children to understand the nature of evidence is probably the most important thing we do in science education."

Pupils are motivated and learn when they play 'games'. The excitement of a game keeps them interested and learning happens almost without them realising that it is happening. Activities like this are an excellent use of time in terms of the learning that can take place.

However, although there are ideas for teaching the content of science through familiar games such as word chase, there are few games to teach pupils about the skills of scientific enquiry. This book aims to fill that gap with a series of creative and stimulating scientific enquiry games.

BUILDING TALK INTO THE GAMES

Pupils talk much more readily about the content of science than the skills. At the end of an investigation, they are much more likely to tell you what they found out than how they got their evidence. Research by Robin Alexander *(Towards Dialogic Teaching, Re-thinking Classroom Talk*. Dialogos.2006) highlights just how important it is to get pupils talking to each other in an informal way. If we want pupils to make progress in scientific skills then we must let them discuss the use and the purpose of these skills with each other. All the games have opportunities for pupils to talk about the skills of science. If you never thought you'd see a group of pupils animatedly discussing the factors involved in fair test investigations, try playing the Fair Test Scramble. You will be amazed!

DIFFERENT WAYS TO PLAY THE GAMES

Because classrooms and laboratories work in different ways, for most of the games we have provided more than one version. If it is difficult for pupils to move around in your setting, fear not. The games can also be played on table-tops or shared using the PDF on a whiteboard. There are also some paper activities related to the skills where appropriate. Use these before the game to introduce ideas or after the game to help pupils recognise for themselves what they have learnt.

RESOURCES

Each game comes with all the written resources that you need to play it. They are also available as PDF versions on the enclosed CD. The CD allows you to make use of the interactive whiteboard tools and to print copies direct from the CD.

All you need to do now is get playing and enjoy watching your pupils learn scientific enquiry skills.

KEY TO SYMBOLS	
	Pupil Material
	Teacher Material
	Pupil and Teacher Material
	Additional Activity

List of Games

Planning

Planning Posers

Planning

Planning Posers

WHAT IS IT?

In this game pupils are given a question that links to an investigation. They have to work out which one of four methods (doing a fair test, pattern seeking, classifying and ordering, or observing/measuring something over time) they would use to answer the question and how they would present the evidence they have collected (table, bar chart, line graph, scatter graph). The teacher puts labels for the different ways of finding out in the four corners of the room. At the teacher's call, a runner, nominated from each group of pupils, goes to the corner of the room that their group has chosen, and adopts a pose to signify the way their group thinks that the results should be presented (e.g. table - hands forming a T, bar chart - standing straight arms tight by side, line graph - arms spread at an angle to represent a line, or scatter graph - fists punching the air in different places).

WHY IS IT IMPORTANT?

Planning how to go about an investigation is an important scientific skill. Pupils need to be able to select the best way of carrying out a scientific enquiry. It is also useful for them to think ahead to the way their evidence will be presented.

Pupils need to know:

- that there are several kinds of investigation, not just fair tests.
- that deciding which kind of investigation to use is an important step when planning an enquiry.
- that there are several ways to present results and that they need to select the one that is appropriate for their investigation.

RESOURCES
Available in the book and on CD

Resource	Page
KINDS OF INVESTIGATION GLOSSARY (Versions 1-3: one per group)	P11
PRESENTING EVIDENCE SHEETS (Versions 1-3: one set per group)	P12-15
QUESTIONS (Versions 1-3: teacher only, can be cut up)	P16-17
INVESTIGATION LABELS (Version 1: for teacher, enlarge to A3 and cut up, Versions 2 and 3: set for each group to cut up)	P18

How to play Planning Posers

HERE ARE SOME DIFFERENT VERSIONS OF THE GAME

Version 1 - Whole class

- Put up the 'Investigation labels' (p18) one in each corner of the room.
- Let pupils discuss these briefly to make sure that they understand each type of investigation and method of presenting evidence. You could give them the 'Glossary' (p11) and the 'Different ways of presenting evidence' (p12-15) to help the discussion.
- Call out a 'Question' (p16-17).
- Groups discuss which of the four types of investigation they would use to answer the question, and how they would present their evidence.
- Ask each group to choose a representative to show their decisions.
- Call out "Posers - to your positions".
- The representatives go to the appropriate corner to show their choice of investigation and 'pose' in the relevant position to show how they would present their results (see introduction for suggestions).

Version 2 - At desks

- Play the game as in Version 1 without putting labels on the walls.
- Instead of individuals running to a corner, the whole group stands up, one pupil holds up an 'Investigation label' (p18) and the rest strike a pose showing how they would present their results.
- Compare the choices and discuss differences asking groups to justify their decisions. Repeat for different questions.

Version 3 - CD & Whiteboard

- Open the 'Planning Poser' activity on the CD. Select the 'Poser Matching' page showing the questions, kinds of investigations and ways of presenting evidence.
- Choose a question.
- As soon as a group has made a decision they strike a pose. One pupil from each group comes to the front and joins the question with the 'Kind of investigation' and 'Way of presenting evidence', using different coloured whiteboard pens if possible.
- Compare responses and discuss differences. Could there be more than one answer?

Planning Posers (Version 1)

Background notes

The four kinds of investigation used in this game are the ones that are most common in science for pupils aged 11-14; there are others. Spend a little time thinking about the different kinds of investigation and looking at examples of each one (see 'Glossary' p11).

You could also talk about ways of presenting evidence (see examples p12-15). Pupils are likely to be familiar with the table, bar chart and line graph. You may need to introduce the scatter graph as it is less frequently used.

SCIENCE QUESTIONS TO CALL OUT (other responses may be possible)		
QUESTION	**KIND OF INVESTIGATION**	**WAY OF PRESENTING EVIDENCE**
Which material keeps a cup of tea warmest after 10 minutes?	Fair test	Bar chart
How many of each type of plant live in and around a pond?	Classifying and ordering	Table
What will happen to the temperature of stearic acid / salol if we let it cool down and take its temperature every minute?	Observing and measuring over time	Line graph
How does changing the amount of sugar in dough affect how much it rises?	Fair test	Line graph
Do taller people have wider arm spans?	Pattern seeking	Scatter graph
How does the strength of an electromagnet change when you alter the electric current going through it?	Fair test	Line graph
Do bigger holly leaves have more prickles?	Pattern seeking	Scatter graph
How does the temperature of a pond vary with the time of day?	Observing and measuring over time	Line graph
How rapidly do different metals react with water?	Classifying and ordering	Table
How does the rate of reaction between acid and marble chips change as the concentration of the acid changes?	Fair test	Line graph
How does the moisture level in soil affect the number of each type of plant in different parts of the school field?	Pattern seeking	Scatter graph

Kinds of Investigation

Glossary

Kind of investigation	Description	Example of this kind of investigation
Doing a fair test	In a fair test, you change one variable to find out what happens to something else. You only change one variable and keep all the other variables the same.	How does the rate of photosynthesis in pondweed change as the light intensity varies?
Pattern seeking	When pattern seeking, you record things you observe or measure and look to see if they are linked. You often use this approach when you want to find things out about people, or plants and animals in their environment.	Do taller trees have bigger leaves?
Classifying and ordering	You classify things when you sort them into groups. Sometimes we sort things into different groups because they have different features, like materials or animals. Sometimes we order things into groups because they behave in different ways.	How can we group these different leaves? Are these materials attracted to the magnet or not?
Observing and measuring over time	Sometimes you find things out by watching one thing over a period of time – you could watch it for a few minutes or a few weeks. Sometimes we just make observations and sometimes we can measure what is happening using equipment.	How does the vitamin C content of fruit juices vary over a month? How does the weight of a piglet change as it grows during the first three months?

Presenting Evidence 1
Tables

Tables can be used in many ways. They can have two or more columns. They can have words or numbers in them. Here are two examples of tables. These can be helpful when you are doing **fair tests, surveys, observing over time** and **classifying**.

How does fertiliser affect the growth of carrots?	
AMOUNT OF FERTILISER (g per sq m)	MASS OF CARROTS (kg)
0	3.0
20	5.5
40	7.5
60	8.5
80	8.0
100	7.5

How does the load in a container affect the force needed to start it moving?	
MASS IN CONTAINER (g)	FORCE TO GET IT JUST MOVING (N)
100	0.2
200	0.4
300	0.6
400	0.9
500	1.2
600	1.5

Presenting Evidence 2

Bar Charts

Bar charts usually have words across the bottom (horizontal axis) and numbers up the side (vertical axis). These can be helpful when you are doing **fair tests** or **surveys**. Here are two examples of a bar chart.

Which antacid tablet is best at neutralising acid?

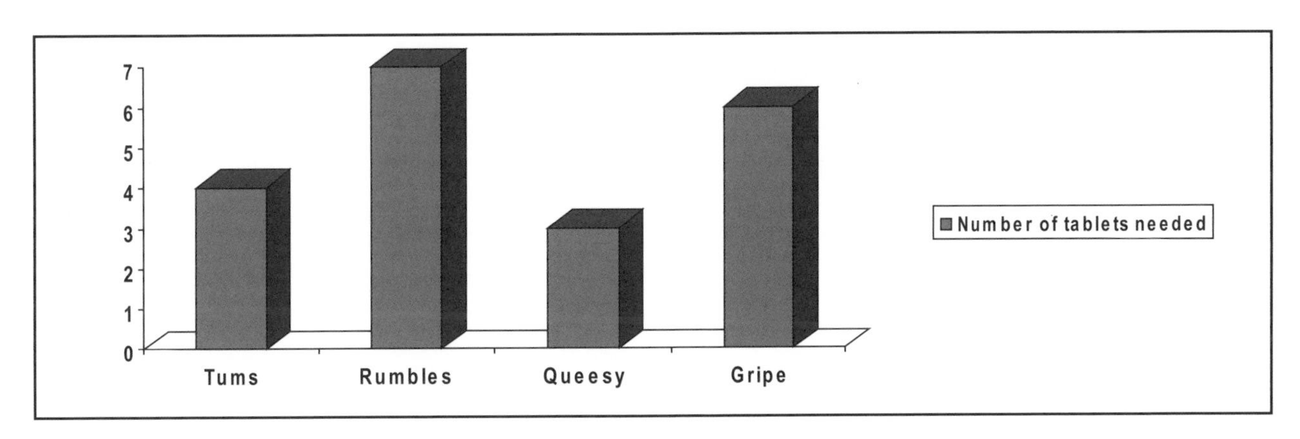

What sort of battery lasts longest?

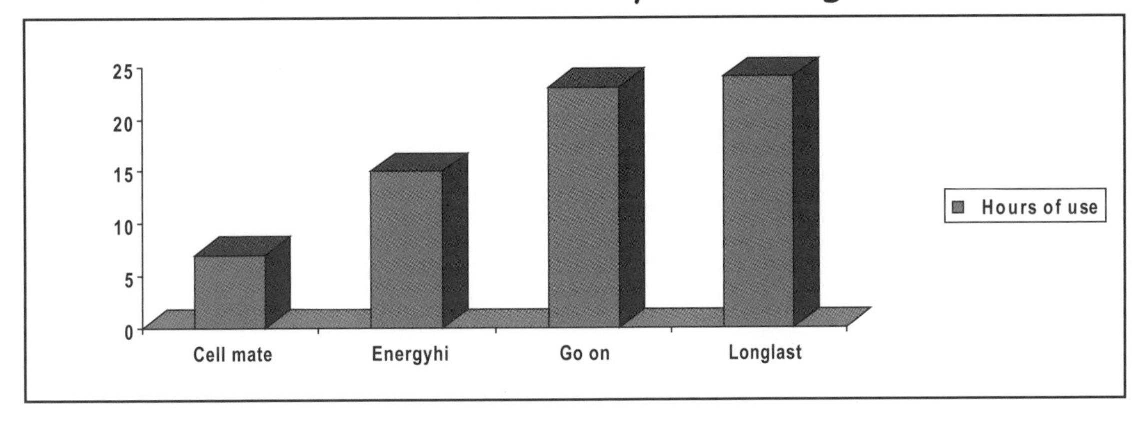

Presenting Evidence 3

Line Graphs

Line graphs have numbers on the bottom (horizontal axis) and up the side (vertical axis). These can be helpful when you are doing **fair tests** and when you are **measuring something over time.** Here are two line graphs.

Stretching a spring

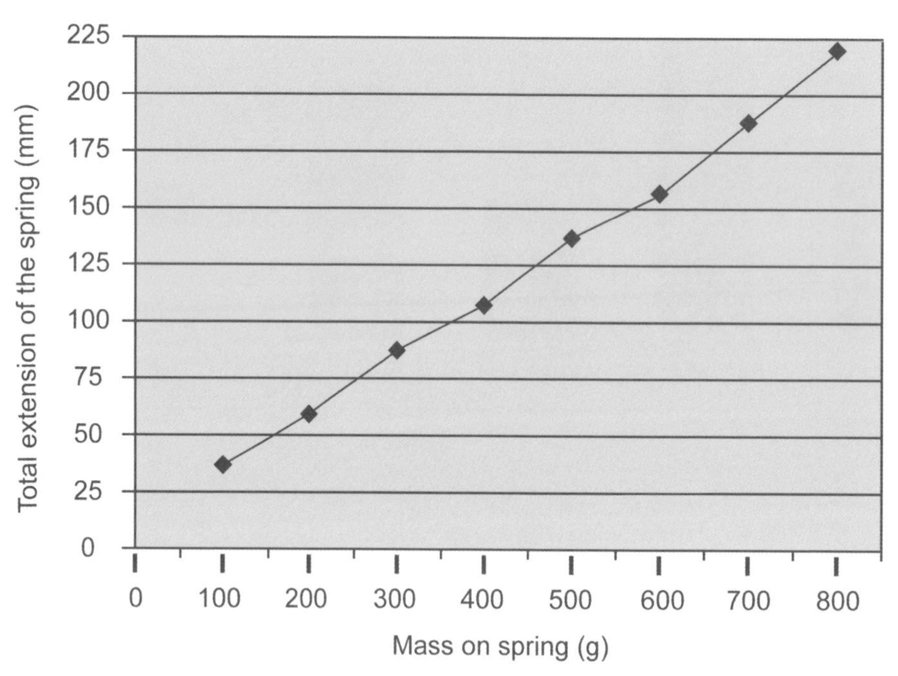

Growing sunflowers

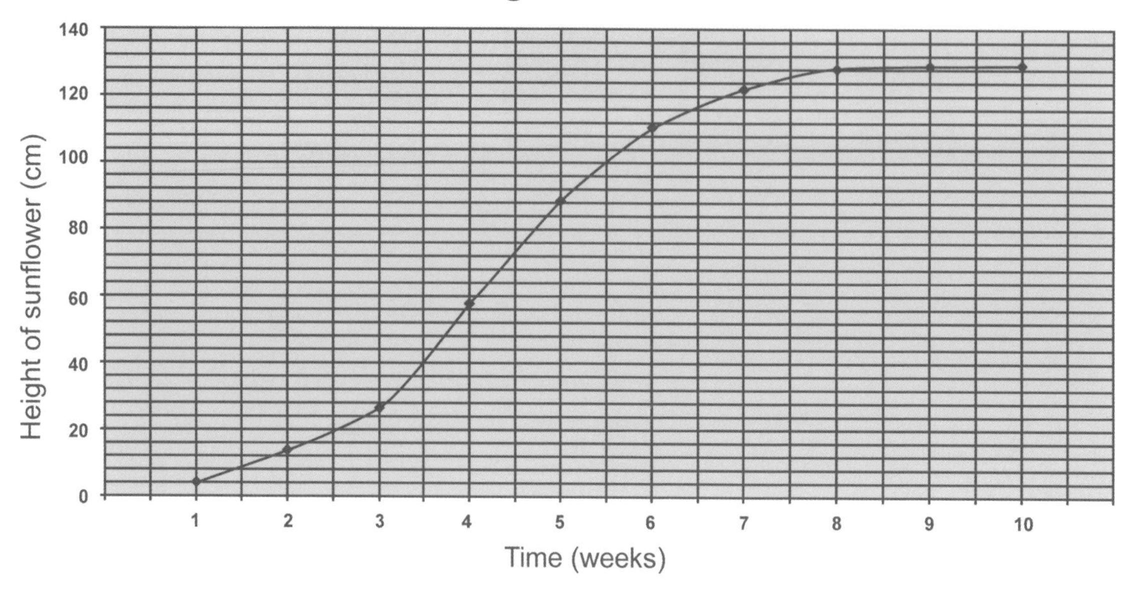

Presenting Evidence 4

Scatter Graphs

In a scatter graph, each dot represents one person or thing. You plot the dots to see whether there is a connection between two sets of data. These can be helpful when you are doing **pattern seeking**.

How does people's hearing vary with age?

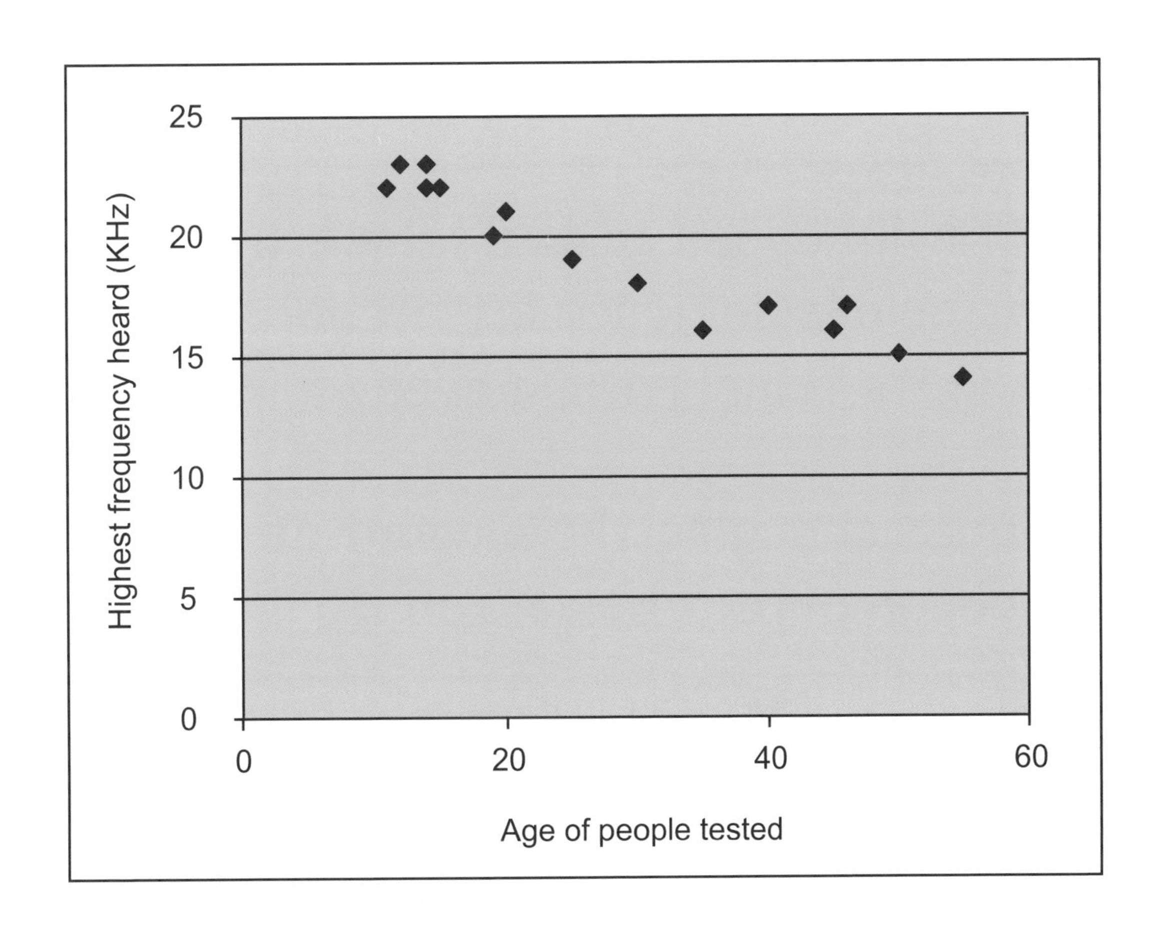

Questions

Can be cut up and used individually.

Which material keeps a cup of tea warmest after 10 minutes?
How many of each type of plant live in and around a pond?
What will happen to the temperature of stearic acid/salol if we let it cool down and take its temperature every minute?
How does changing the amount of sugar in dough affect how much it rises?
Do taller people have wider arm spans?
How does the strength of an electromagnet change when you alter the electric current going through it?

Do bigger holly leaves have more prickles?
How does the temperature of a pond vary with the time of day?
How rapidly do different metals react with water?
How does the rate of reaction between acid and marble chips change as the concentration of the acid changes?
How does the moisture level in soil affect the number of each type of plant in different parts of the school field?

Investigation labels

Enlarge to A3 and cut up to put in the corners of the classroom.
Use as A4 on pupils' tables.

Classifying and ordering

Fair test

Pattern seeking

Observing and measuring over time

Fair Testing

Fair Test Scramble

Fair Testing

Fair Test Scramble

WHAT IS IT?

In this game groups are given a number of variables from different investigations. The teacher announces a question that might be suitable for a fair test investigation. Each group has to select the variables (what we should change, measure and keep the same) that apply in that investigation. The words CHANGE, MEASURE, KEEP THE SAME are posted in accessible places around the room. The teacher calls out one of the words. A runner from each group scrambles, or races, to the correct place with the relevant variable card or cards.

WHY IS IT IMPORTANT?

Pupils are generally aware of the need for fair tests but do not always understand that it involves changing one variable in order to see the effect this has on another. They may know the fair test principle but have difficulty applying this in new situations. The game gives them plenty of opportunity to practise planning fair tests in a variety of contexts without carrying out the investigation every time.

Pupils need to know:

- why it is important to change just one variable. If more than one variable is changed then it is difficult to know which caused the effect.
- why changing and measuring helps them to organise tables, charts and graphs.
- the difference between something that is measured to make sure that it is kept the same, and something that is measured as it alters during the experiment. The terms control, independent and dependent variable need to be introduced. This is best done when pupils have a good understanding of the fair test principles.

RESOURCES Available in the book and on CD	
INVESTIGATION PICTURES (Version 1: one set per group)	P25
VARIABLE CARDS (Version 1 and 3: one set per group, Version 2: teacher only)	P26 P27
QUESTIONS (Version 1 and 3: teacher only)	P28 P29
LABELS (Version 1 and 2: for teacher, photocopied on A3 and cut up)	P30
YOU WILL ALSO NEED Wipe boards and pens	

How to play Fair Test Scramble

HERE ARE SOME DIFFERENT VERSIONS OF THE GAME

Version 1 - Whole class

- Put the large 'Labels' CHANGE, MEASURE and KEEP THE SAME (p30) in easily accessible places. Give each group the 'Variable cards' (p26-27).
- Talk about the investigations in the 'Investigation pictures' (p25).
- Call out a 'Question' from the list (p28-29).
- Allow a little time to discuss what they would CHANGE, MEASURE and KEEP THE SAME in order to answer the question.
- Call out "Get ready to scramble ...." followed by one of the words on one of the labels e.g. "...CHANGE"
- A runner grabs the 'Variable card' that their group has decided will be changed and runs to the label.
- The first runner to put the correct 'Variable card' against the label wins a point for their team. Compare the chosen variables and discuss any differences.

Version 2 - Groups

- Ask one group to stand with a 'Variable card' by each label, for example:
  CHANGE - distance object is from light.
  MEASURE - length of shadow.
  KEEP THE SAME - height of object.
- Ask the rest of the class to discuss what the question might be. For example, "Does the distance between the object and the light make a difference to the length of the shadow?". Each group could write their question on a wipe board.
- Choose one board at a time and ask the rest of the class to decide if it could be a correct answer. Each group that finds a question that fits gains one point.

Version 3 - CD & Whiteboard

- Open the 'Fair Test Scramble' activity on the CD at the 'Variable' page. Give the pupils 'Variable cards' (p26-27) and play as in version 1.
- The runner comes to the board and ticks the variable using the whiteboard pen.
- Compare the chosen variables and discuss any differences.

Extra Activity

At the end of this section (p31-32) you will find two examples of investigations where fair testing is important. You can discuss these with pupils, either to introduce the game or to review their understanding afterwards.

Fair Test Scramble (Version 1)

Background notes

The following list suggests questions that you could use in Fair Test Scramble, plus possible answers.

QUESTION TO INVESTIGATE	ANSWERS		
	Change Independent Variable	**Measure** Dependent Variable	**Keep the same** Control Variables
How many antacid tablets are needed to neutralise acid?	*Type of antacid tablet*	*Number of tablets needed to neutralise acid*	*Concentration of acid, volume of acid, temperature of acid*
How does the time a candle burns depend on the size of container it is in?	*Volume of jar*	*Time before candle goes out*	*Height of candle, diameter of candle, length of wick*
How does the amount of fertiliser affect the growth of seedlings?	*Mass of fertiliser applied*	*Height of seedling*	*Volume of water given, temperature of surroundings, time since germination*
How does the depth of crater formed when a ball is dropped into sand depend on the height from which it is dropped?	*Height from which ball is dropped*	*Depth of crater*	*Size of ball, mass of ball, type of sand*
How does the number of antacid tablets needed to neutralise acid vary with the volume of acid?	*Volume of acid*	*Number of tablets needed to neutralise acid*	*Concentration of acid, temperature of acid, type of antacid tablet*
How does the height of a candle affect the time for which it burns?	*Height of candle*	*Time before candle goes out*	*Diameter of candle, length of wick, volume of jar*
How does the amount of water given affect the growth of a seedling?	*Volume of water given*	*Height of seedling*	*Mass of fertiliser applied, temperature of surroundings, time since germination*
How does the depth of crater formed when a ball is dropped into sand depend on the mass of the ball?	*Mass of ball*	*Depth of crater*	*Size of ball, height from which ball is dropped, type of sand*

Investigation Pictures

These are the four investigations the pupils carried out.

How good are antacid tablets at neutralising acid?

What affects how long a candle burns?

What affects the rate at which seedlings grow?

What affects the depth of crater formed when a ball is dropped into sand?

Variable Cards

You need to cut out the cards.

Type of antacid tablet
Number of tablets needed to neutralise acid
Concentration of acid
Volume of acid
Temperature of acid
Volume of jar
Time before candle goes out
Height of candle
Diameter of candle

Length of wick
Mass of fertiliser applied
Volume of water given
Height of seedling
Temperature of surroundings
Time since germination
Height from which ball is dropped
Depth of crater
Size of ball
Mass of ball
Type of sand

Questions

How many antacid tablets are needed to neutralise acid?
How does the time a candle burns depend on the size of container it is in?
How does the amount of fertiliser affect the growth of seedlings?
How does the depth of crater formed when a ball is dropped into sand depend on the height from which it is dropped?

How does the number of antacid tablets needed to neutralise acid vary with the volume of acid?
How does the height of a candle affect the time for which it burns?
How does the amount of water given affect the growth of a seedling?
How does the depth of crater formed when a ball is dropped into sand depend on the mass of the ball?

Labels

Enlarge to A3 and cut up to put around the classroom.

Change **(Independent variable)**
Measure **(Dependent variable)**
Keep the same **(Control variables)**

Roof Insulation

Ahmed, Aisha and Andy were trying to find out which material would be the best to insulate a roof. They had four different materials: polystyrene, vermiculite, mineral fibre and foil-lined plasterboard. They placed a layer of each one over a beaker of hot water.

Which variable were they changing?

Which variable were they measuring to get their results?

Which variables were they keeping the same?

Making Bread Rise

Sean, Sadie and Shamila were making bread using flour, yeast, salt and water. They were trying to find out if adding sugar will help to make the dough rise, and if so, does it make a difference how much they use. They made four different batches of dough with the same quantities of each ingredient apart from the sugar. Some of each batch was put in one of four beakers, enough to cover the bottom, and then the beakers were left in a warm place to let the dough rise.

Which variable were they changing?

Which variable were they measuring to get their results?

Which variables were they keeping the same?

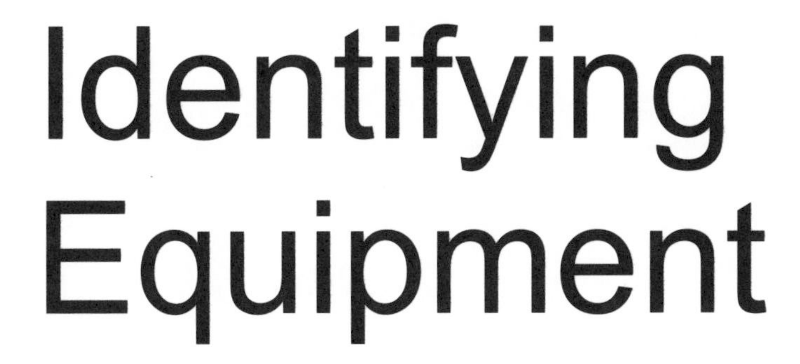

Identifying Equipment

Getting the Gear

Identifying Equipment

Getting the Gear

3

WHAT IS IT?

In this game pupils play a 'Happy Families' style game and collect sets of investigations and related equipment. They work together in groups of 4, 6 or 8 and are dealt playing cards showing 36 different pieces of equipment and 12 questions that could be investigated. The challenge is to collect 'families' consisting of one question card and three pieces of equipment needed to carry out a practical enquiry. Pupils need to think about scales as well as the item of equipment. The pair that collects most complete 'families' of equipment wins.

WHY IS IT IMPORTANT?

Choosing the right equipment for an experiment is vital to its success yet it is not always realistic in a school laboratory to provide pupils with much choice. Pupils need to be taught how important it is to think in advance exactly how to go about an investigation.

Pupils need to be able to:

- decide in advance how a scientific question might be answered, and the likely range of any measurements, in order to choose instruments correctly.
- think carefully about the equipment needed to get the most precise results.
- consider and comment on the equipment in order to appreciate that scientific research techniques are subject to peer scrutiny.
- understand what a particular piece of equipment is used for, and how they might use it appropriately.
- appreciate that some equipment comes with different scales to allow for more precise measurements or to measure larger objects.

RESOURCES Available in the book and on CD	
CARDS *(Version 1: one pack of 48 cards per group of 4, 6 or 8. Version 2: one pack- dealt between all the groups)*	P42-53
INVESTIGATION LIST (Version 1: one per pair, Version 2: one per group)	P40
EQUIPMENT LIST *(Version 1: one per pair, Version 2: one per group)*	P41

How to play Getting the Gear

HERE ARE SOME DIFFERENT VERSIONS OF THE GAME

Version 1 - Groups

- Cut out enough 'Packs of cards' (p42-53) to make a set for each group in the class - groups of 4 (playing individually), 6 or 8 (playing in pairs).

- Each group deals out all the cards, face down, to the players, or pairs of players, in their group. Every card needs to be used even if some pupils end up with more than others.

- Give players the 'Equipment list' (p41) and the 'Investigation' list (p40).

- The players look at their cards and the 'Equipment' and 'Investigation' lists and, if in pairs, discuss which families would be best to collect.

- The first player asks another pair for a particular card in a family. This could be the investigation title or a piece of equipment. For example *"Do you have 'How much water drips through different soils in 5 minutes?' please?"*, or *"Do you have a 'Measuring cylinder 0-100 ml' please?"*.

- Players do not include the letter when asking for cards. This would give away too much information.

- Carry on as for Happy Families. Players will know if they have the complete equipment family because they will have 4 cards all with the same letter in the title (A—L).

- The winner is the player(s) with the most full sets of investigation questions and equipment at the end of the game.

Version 2 - Whole Class

- Play as above but deal out cards across the whole class.

- Each table discusses what they are going to ask for and which table to ask.

Getting the Gear (Version 1)

Background notes

There are 48 cards in a pack; 12 sets or 'Equipment families', each consisting of one 'Investigation card' and three 'Apparatus cards'. 'Equipment families' are lettered A to L on the face side so that players can recognise when they have called correctly. The CD also includes cards without the letters A to L.

It is possible to invent other games using these cards.

OTHER GAMES

(1) Pupils can be given the complete set of cards and asked to try to make families of one question and three equipment cards, without the letter clues to suggest which go together. When they have created their families, can they justify their groupings? Can they come up with other questions that might be answered by using the same set of equipment? A point for every 'happy family' that they make.

(2) The questions are removed from two packs leaving just the apparatus cards. These packs are combined giving a total of 72 cards. Players are dealt nine cards each and the remaining cards are left face down in the centre. Players are given two opportunities to 'twist' (swap a card for the top card in the pack) or 'stick' (make no change).

Players are then given time to think about how the equipment might be grouped in sets of three and the question that might be answered using each group of equipment. Players then show their hands and have to explain how their cards will help to answer the scientific question that they have chosen. There is a point for each appropriate set and the player(s) who uses most cards wins the round and gains a bonus point. There is a point deducted for each piece of equipment not used. The game can be played for three or four rounds.

Background notes continued

Overview of the questions and equipment.

	QUESTION	EQUIPMENT
A	How does fertiliser affect the growth of pondweed? (You are given samples of duckweed and fertiliser)	Plastic fish tank Digital scales (0.1 g intervals) Hand lens
B	How much water drips through different soils in 5 minutes? (You are given some different soils and a stopclock)	Measuring cylinder (0-100 ml) Glass or plastic funnels Filter paper
C	How does putting different masses in a trainer affect the force needed to move it up a ramp? (You are given a trainer)	Masses (5 x 0.5 kg masses) Forcemeter (0-100 N) Wooden ramp
D	How does temperature affect the amount of salt that will dissolve in water? (You are given salt and water)	Thermometer (-10-100^{0}C) Spatula or measuring spoon Bunsen, tripod and gauze
E	What plants grow in different parts of the school field? (You are given a clip-board)	Large mounted magnifier Plant key Quadrat (or wooden frame)
F	How does increasing the number of lamps in a circuit affect the current? (You are given connecting leads)	Ammeter (0-1 amps) Lamps and lamp holders Power supply (0-6 Volts)
G	How does changing the mass on the end of an elastic band affect its length? (You are given an elastic band)	Masses (10 x 100 g) Metre rule (with cm and mm divisions) Clampstand and boss
H	How does the strength of an electromagnet change with the current flowing through it? (You are given flexible wire and leads)	Paper clips Large steel nail Ammeter (0-5 amps)
I	Which fruit juices make the best battery? (You are given an orange, lemon and grapefruit or their juice)	Voltmeter (0-5 V) Leads, crocodile clips and small lamp Strips of different metals
J	How does the colour of light affect the rate at which pondweed makes oxygen? (You are given elodea pondweed and a large beaker)	'Desk' lamp Colour filters Measuring cylinder (0-10 ml)
K	Do dark things heat up and cool down more quickly than light shiny ones? (You are given a thermometer and tin cans)	Foil and black paint Radiant heater Stop clock (seconds and minutes)
L	How does drinking cola or coffee affect your reaction time? (You are given cola or coffee and a low voltage power supply)	Electronic timer (hundredths of a second) Lamp and buzzer Switches

Investigation List

A	How does fertiliser affect the growth of pondweed? (You are given samples of duckweed and fertiliser)
B	How much water drips through different soils in 5 minutes? (You are given some different soils and a stopclock)
C	How does putting different masses in a trainer affect the force needed to move it up a ramp? (You are given a trainer)
D	How does temperature affect the amount of salt that will dissolve in water? (You are given salt and water)
E	What plants grow in different parts of the school field? (You are given a clip-board)
F	How does increasing the number of lamps in a circuit affect the current? (You are given connecting leads)
G	How does changing the mass on the end of an elastic band affect its length? (You are given an elastic band)
H	How does the strength of an electromagnet change with the current flowing through it? (You are given flexible wire and connecting leads)
I	Which fruit juices make the best battery? (You are given an orange, lemon and grapefruit or their juice)
J	How does the colour of light affect the rate at which pondweed makes oxygen? (You are given elodea pondweed and a large beaker)
K	Do dark things heat up and cool down more quickly than light shiny ones? (You are given a thermometer and tin cans)
L	How does drinking cola or coffee affect your reaction time? (You are given cola or coffee and a low voltage power supply)

Equipment List

A	Plastic fish tank, Digital scales (0.1 g intervals), Hand lens
B	Measuring cylinder (0-100 ml), Glass or plastic funnels, Filter paper
C	Masses (5 x 0.5 kg masses), Forcemeter (0-100 N), Wooden ramp
D	Thermometer (-10-100°C), Spatula or Measuring spoon, Bunsen, Tripod and gauze
E	Large mounted magnifier, Plant key, Quadrat (or wooden frame)
F	Ammeter (0-1 amps), Lamps and lamp holders, Power supply (0-6 Volts)
G	Masses (10 x 100 g), Metre rule (with cm and mm divisions), Clampstand and boss
H	Paper clips, Large steel nail, Ammeter (0-5 amps)
I	Voltmeter (0-5 V), Leads, Crocodile clips and Small lamp, Strips of different metals
J	'Desk' lamp, Colour filters, Measuring cylinder (0-10 ml)
K	Foil and black paint, Radiant heater, Stop clock (seconds and minutes)
L	Electronic timer (hundredths of a second), Lamp and buzzer, Switches

How does fertiliser affect the growth of pondweed?

(YOU ARE GIVEN SAMPLES OF DUCKWEED & FERTILISER)

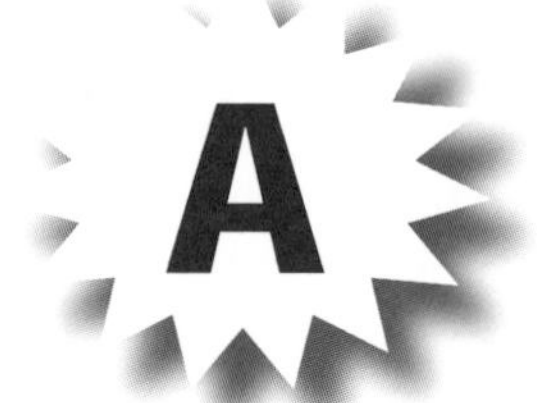

Plastic fish tank

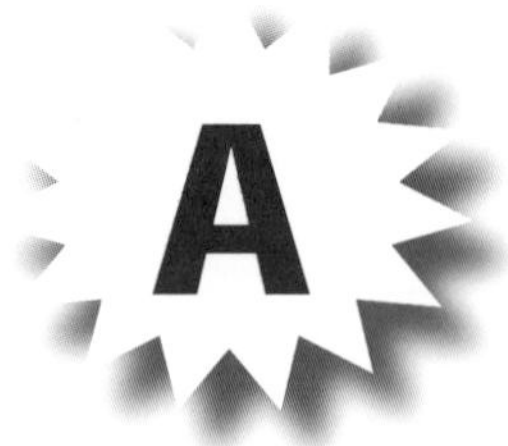

Digital scales (0.1 g intervals)

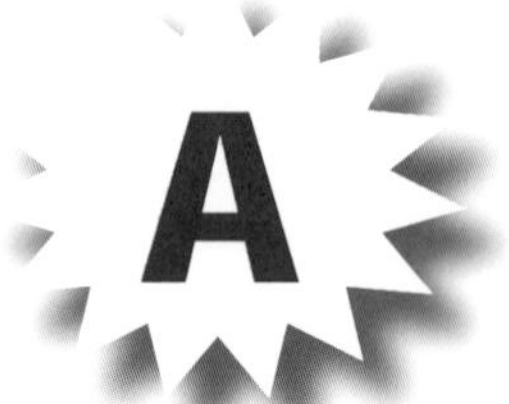

Hand lens

How much water drips through different soils in 5 minutes?

(YOU ARE GIVEN SOME DIFFERENT SOILS & A STOPCLOCK)

Measuring cylinder (0-100 ml)

Glass or plastic funnels

Filter paper

How does putting different masses in a trainer affect the force needed to move it up a ramp?

(YOU ARE GIVEN A TRAINER)

Masses (5 x 0.5 kg masses)

Forcemeter (0-100 N)

Wooden ramp

How does temperature affect the amount of salt that will dissolve in water?

(YOU ARE GIVEN SALT AND WATER)

Thermometer (-10-100°C)

Spatula or measuring spoon

Bunsen, tripod and gauze

What plants grow in different parts of the school field?

(YOU ARE GIVEN A CLIP-BOARD)

Large mounted magnifier

Plant key

Quadrat (or wooden frame)

How does increasing the number of lamps in a circuit affect the current?

(YOU ARE GIVEN CONNECTING LEADS)

Ammeter (0-1 amps)

Lamps and lamp holders

Power supply (0-6 Volts)

How does changing the mass on the end of an elastic band affect its length?

(YOU ARE GIVEN AN ELASTIC BAND)

Masses (10 x 100 g)

Metre rule (with cm and mm divisions)

Clampstand and boss

How does the strength of an electromagnet change with the current flowing through it?

(YOU ARE GIVEN FLEXIBLE WIRE AND LEADS)

Paper clips

Large steel nail

Ammeter (0-5 amps)

Which fruit juices make the best battery?

(YOU ARE GIVEN AN ORANGE, LEMON AND GRAPEFRUIT OR THEIR JUICE)

Voltmeter (0-5 V)

Leads, crocodile clips and small lamp

Strips of different metals

How does the colour of light affect the rate at which pondweed makes oxygen?

(YOU ARE GIVEN ELODEA PONDWEED AND A LARGE BEAKER)

'Desk' lamp

Colour filters

Measuring cylinder (0-10 ml)

Do dark things heat up and cool down more quickly than light shiny ones?

(YOU ARE GIVEN A THERMOMETER AND TIN CANS)

Foil and black paint

Radiant heater

Stop clock (seconds and minutes)

How does drinking cola or coffee affect your reaction time?

(YOU ARE GIVEN COLA OR COFFEE AND A LOW VOLTAGE POWER SUPPLY)

Electronic timer (hundredths of a second)

Lamp and buzzer

Switches

Repeat
Readings
Rumble
4

Repeat Readings

Rumble

WHAT IS IT?

In this game, pupils see which group can get the most reliable data using the least amount of money. Each group is given money to buy pieces of data about repeat tests carried out in an investigation (e.g. the absorbency of paper towels). Groups decide how much money to spend to get enough data to be able to work out a reliable value of the mean average. Groups get bonus payouts according to how close their result is to the mean average of six results. There is also an extension activity which allows pupils to discard one outlying result from their set of repeat readings (see p67).

WHY IS IT IMPORTANT?

This game helps pupils understand that repeating a test gives you better quality evidence. It also brings out the point that in commercial situations, companies have to balance the need for reliable readings against the costs involved for each test.

Pupils sometimes mistakenly think that:

- they take repeat readings to make it a fair test.
- if investigations are carried out carefully, they do not need to repeat any of the readings.
- repeating a reading makes it more accurate. (Accuracy is always limited by the precision of the measuring equipment. For example, if you are using a ruler that measures in whole centimetres you will not be able to get a more accurate result by repeating the test. You will still only be able to measure in centimetres not in more precise millimetres.)

RESOURCES

Available in the book and on CD

Resource	Pages
PUPILS' TABLES OF RESULTS partly completed (Version 1: set for each group. NB There are 3 different tables - choose which one/s you want to use)	P61 P63 P65
TEACHER'S TABLES OF RESULTS completed (Version 1 and 2: teacher only)	P62 P64 P66
MONEY SHEETS (Version 1: 20 X 10 rumble notes for each group plus bonus money) *(Version 2: two sets of 20 x 10 rumble notes plus bonus money. Alternatively use monopoly money or counters)*	P69-70
YOU WILL ALSO NEED One calculator per group	

How to play Rumble

HERE ARE SOME DIFFERENT VERSIONS OF THE GAME

Version 1 - Groups

- Give each group 20 x 10 'Rumble notes' (200 rumbles) (p69) and a 'Table of results' (p61, 63 and 65) with the first reading completed. You can use counters or monopoly money.
- Ask each group in turn whether they want to buy any results for the second reading. Collect 10 rumbles from each group for each result requested.
- Read out the results for the second reading. The groups enter them on their tables.
- Allow time for them to decide whether to buy more results for each paper towel in the next round, then repeat as before.
- If a group decides to stick for any paper towel, they put a line through the remaining spaces for that towel. Then they work out the mean average for the readings they have and put that in the final column.
- Repeat as before until all groups have bought all the readings they want and calculated their mean averages for each towel.
- Tell them the final mean averages shown on the 'Teacher's table of results'.
- Hand out 'bonus' payments and then find out which group has the most money. NB See extension on p67.

Version 2 - CD & Whiteboard

- Put up a partly completed 'Table of results' on the whiteboard.
- Put out two equal piles of money (at least 200 rumbles) - one belonging to the class and one to you as the banker.
- The class votes whether to buy data from you. Fill this in on the table and transfer money as appropriate.
- When all buying is complete, work out the mean averages for the class and compare these with the final mean averages shown on the teacher's table.
- Hand out previously agreed bonuses to the class for how close they were to the final mean averages.
- Compare money total for banker and class.

Extra Activity

At the end of this section (p71) you will find an extra activity , 'Do it Again', to use for discussion with the pupils before or after playing the game.

Rumble (Version 1)

Background notes

Each game is likely to take at least 20 mins for each table.

After one game, discuss the tactics used by each team. The following questions may help:

- Why did you stop buying results?
- Was this the right decision? Why?
- How many results did you need to get a good idea of the final result?
- Was it the same for each towel? Why?
- Which would you trust more - a mean average of 10 results or 2 results? Why?
- If more readings give more reliable results, why don't scientists always take hundreds of readings?

NOTES FOR EXTRA ACTIVITY (P71)

This can be used to generate discussions about repeat readings before or after the game.

Two key points should emerge:

- Repeat readings are more important when there is likely to be some variation than when results are likely to be very similar.
- One way to evaluate how much results can be trusted is to look at the variation between readings.

PART 1 - Comparing two investigations:

- the height of a bounce (repeat readings are likely to show some variation)
- the length of a shadow (repeat readings are unlikely to show variation)

To extend the activity, give pairs a list of familiar investigations such as:

- how long different toy parachutes take to fall
- how long different sugars take to dissolve
- how much elastic stretches with different loads
- how long it takes a candle to go out under different sized jars

Pupils rate the importance of repeat readings (from 1 = fairly unimportant to 5 = very important).

PART 2 - What to look for to decide the number of readings could include:

- how likely it would be to get similar results from their repeat readings
- the time available
- whether equipment can be re-used etc.

PART 3 - Use the two tables to compare repeat readings that are closely clustered (with larger measuring divisions) or more spread out (with finer measuring divisions).

Encourage pupils to look at the spread of repeat readings when evaluating their own results.

Set 1

Pupils' Table of Results

You work for a company that wants to manufacture paper towels. The towels need to be absorbent. Your company wants some results about the performance of the other paper towels on the market. You need to get as reliable results as possible for the least amount of money.

Your task is to work out what you think is the mean average amount of water absorbed by each type of paper towel. The paper towels have been tested by putting the same sized sheets in a measuring cylinder of 50 ml of water, removing them and then calculating how much water they have soaked up. The first reading for each type of paper towel is given in your table.

You will be given some money and you can buy the results of other tests (repeat readings). You can stop buying results at any time and work out the mean average of your results. Because it will help your business, you will get extra money at the end depending on how close your answers are to the actual results. For each answer that is within 0.2 ml you will get a 50 rumbles bonus, and if your answer is within 0.4 ml you will get a 20 rumbles bonus. You will need to weigh up whether it is worth spending more money to get more information or whether you have enough data to be able to work out a reliable value of the mean averages.

Type of paper towel	AMOUNT OF WATER ABSORBED BY PAPER TOWEL (ml)						Mean Average
	1st Reading	2nd Reading	3rd Reading	4th Reading	5th Reading	6th Reading	
Bouncy	19.6						
Quilter	17.9						
Softee	16.2						
Diamond	17.5						

Set 1

Teacher's Table of Results

Type of paper towel	AMOUNT OF WATER ABSORBED BY PAPER TOWEL (ml)						Mean Average
	1st Reading	2nd Reading	3rd Reading	4th Reading	5th Reading	6th Reading	
Bouncy	19.6	20.2	20.1	18.8	19.5	19.6	**19.6**
Quilter	17.9	21.3	22.6	21.7	19.9	22.4	**21.0**
Softee	16.2	17.3	15.8	16.7	17.0	18.1	**16.9**
Diamond	17.5	17.7	18.3	18.9	18.6	18.8	**18.3**

Bonus payments awarded: Answers within 0.2 ml - 50 rumble bonus.
Answers within 0.4 ml - 20 rumble bonus

BONUS BANDS						
0 Rumbles	**20 Rumbles**	**50 Rumbles ml**			**20 Rumbles**	**0 Rumbles**
BOUNCY						
	19.2	19.4	19.6	19.8	20.0	
QUILTER						
	20.6	20.8	21.0	21.2	21.4	
SOFTEE						
	16.5	16.7	16.9	17.1	17.3	
DIAMOND						
	17.9	18.1	18.3	18.5	18.7	

(All answers rounded to 1 decimal place)

Set 2

Pupils' Table of Results

Your task is to work out what you think is the most likely dry strength for each type of paper. The papers have been tested by stretching them over a container and adding masses until they tear. The total mass in kg held by each paper has been noted down. The first reading for each type of paper is given in your table.

You will be given some money and you can buy the results of other tests (repeat readings). You can stop buying results at any time and work out the mean average of your results. You will get extra money at the end depending on how close your answers are to the actual results. If your answer is within 0.02 kg you will get a 50 rumbles bonus and if your answer is within 0.04 kg you will get a 20 rumbles bonus. You will need to weigh up whether it is worth spending more money to get more information or whether you have enough data to be able to work out a reliable value of the mean averages.

Type of paper towel	MASS HELD BY DRY PAPER TOWEL (kg)						Mean Average
	1st Reading	2nd Reading	3rd Reading	4th Reading	5th Reading	6th Reading	
Bouncy	1.89						
Quilter	2.04						
Softee	2.15						
Diamond	1.66						

Set 2

Teacher's Table of Results

Type of paper towel	MASS HELD BY DRY PAPER TOWEL (kg)						Mean Average
	1st Reading	2nd Reading	3rd Reading	4th Reading	5th Reading	6th Reading	
Bouncy	1.89	1.97	2.13	2.17	2.10	2.04	2.05
Quilter	2.04	1.86	1.95	1.96	2.07	1.90	1.96
Softee	2.15	2.24	2.16	1.95	1.99	2.08	2.10
Diamond	1.66	1.84	1.72	1.63	1.65	1.62	1.69

Bonus payments awarded: Answers within 0.02 kg - 50 rumble bonus.
Answers within 0.04 kg - 20 rumble bonus

BONUS BANDS							
0 Rumbles	20 Rumbles	50 Rumbles kg			20 Rumbles	0 Rumbles
BOUNCY						
	2.01	2.03	2.05	2.07	2.09	
QUILTER						
	1.92	1.94	1.96	1.98	2.00	
SOFTEE						
	2.06	2.08	2.10	2.12	2.14	
DIAMOND						
	1.65	1.67	1.69	1.71	1.73	

(All answers rounded to 2 decimal places)

Set 3

Pupils' Table of Results

Your task is to work out what you think is the most likely wet strength for each type of paper towel. The paper towels have been tested by stretching them over a container, dripping water on them until they are wet all over and adding masses until they tear. The total mass in kg held by each paper towel has been noted down. The first reading for each type of paper towel is given in your table.

You will be given some money and you can buy the results of other tests (repeat readings). You can stop buying results at any time and work out the mean average of your results. You will get extra money at the end depending on how close your answers are to the actual results. If your answer is within 0.02 kg you will get a 50 rumbles bonus and if your answer is within 0.04 kg you will get a 20 rumbles bonus. You will need to weigh up whether it is worth spending more money to get more information or whether you have enough data to be able to work out a reliable value of the mean averages.

Type of paper towel	MASS HELD BY WET PAPER TOWEL (kg)						Mean Average
	1st Reading	2nd Reading	3rd Reading	4th Reading	5th Reading	6th Reading	
Bouncy	0.98						
Quilter	0.82						
Softee	0.73						
Diamond	0.88						

Set 3

Teacher's Table of Results

Type of paper towel	MASS HELD BY WET PAPER TOWEL (kg)						Mean Average
	1st Reading	2nd Reading	3rd Reading	4th Reading	5th Reading	6th Reading	
Bouncy	0.98	1.06	0.83	1.06	1.02	0.97	0.99
Quilter	0.82	0.93	0.96	0.95	0.99	0.84	0.92
Softee	0.73	0.77	0.82	0.79	0.78	0.76	0.78
Diamond	0.88	0.97	0.99	0.84	0.96	0.94	0.93

Bonus payments awarded: Answers within 0.02 kg - 50 rumble bonus.
Answers within 0.04 kg - 20 rumble bonus.

BONUS BANDS

0 Rumbles	20 Rumbles	50 Rumbles kg	20 Rumbles	0 Rumbles
		BOUNCY		
	0.95	0.97 0.99 1.01	1.03	
		QUILTER		
	0.88	0.90 0.92 0.94	0.96	
		SOFTEE		
	0.74	0.76 0.78 0.80	0.82	
		DIAMOND		
	0.89	0.91 0.93 0.95	0.97	

(All answers rounded to 2 decimal places)

Extension

Discarding One Result

Once the pupils have decided to stick and have no more results to fill in for any one paper towel, allow them to discard one reading (outlier) from that set of repeat readings. Pupils calculate the mean average from their remaining readings.

When all the pupils have bought all the readings that they want and calculated the mean averages for each towel, read out the final mean averages based on the five remaining readings (ie with the outlier discarded before the mean was calculated).

Hand out bonus payments using the second set of narrower bonus bands (see below and overleaf) and work out which group has the most money.

Bonus bands based on five results when the outlier is removed.

SET 1 BONUS BANDS

0 Rumbles	20 Rumbles	50 Rumbles kg	20 Rumbles	0 Rumbles
		BOUNCY		
	19.6	19.7 19.8 19.9	20.0	
		QUILTER		
	21.4	21.5 21.6 21.7	21.8	
		SOFTEE		
	16.4	16.5 16.6 16.7	16.8	
		DIAMOND		
	18.3	18.4 18.5 18.6	18.7	

(All answers rounded to 1 decimal place)

SET 2 BONUS BANDS

0 Rumbles	20 Rumbles	50 Rumbles kg			20 Rumbles	0 Rumbles
			BOUNCY			
	2.06	2.07	2.08	2.09	2.10	
			QUILTER			
	1.92	1.93	1.94	1.95	1.96	
			SOFTEE			
	2.10	2.11	2.12	2.13	2.14	
			DIAMOND			
	1.64	1.65	1.66	1.67	1.68	

SET 3 BONUS BANDS

0 Rumbles	20 Rumbles	50 Rumbles kg			20 Rumbles	0 Rumbles
			BOUNCY			
	1.00	1.01	1.02	1.03	1.04	
			QUILTER			
	0.91	0.92	0.93	0.94	0.95	
			SOFTEE			
	0.76	0.77	0.78	0.79	0.80	
			DIAMOND			
	0.93	0.94	0.95	0.96	0.97	

(All answers rounded to 2 decimal places)

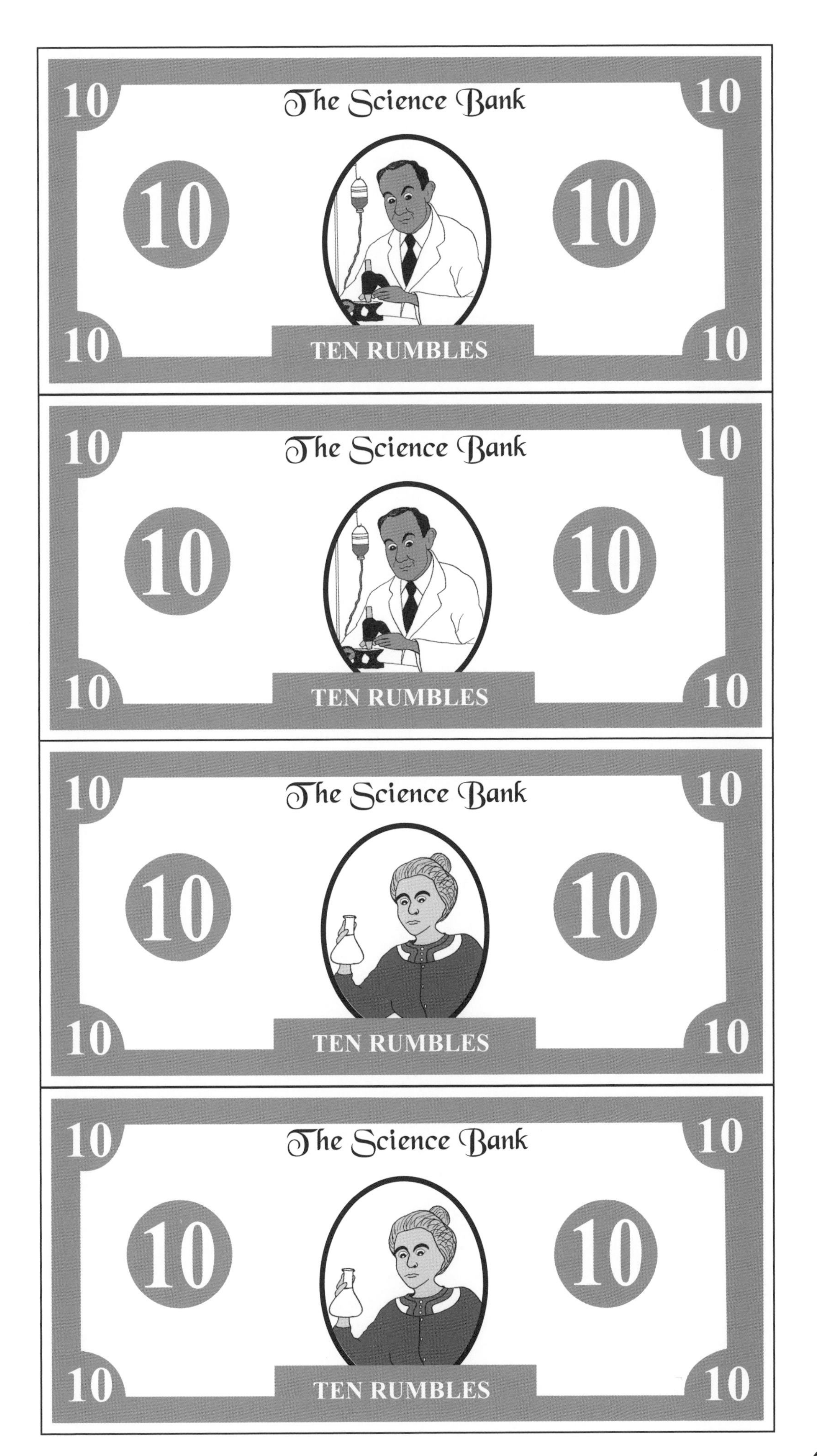
10
The Science Bank
10
10
10
10
10
TEN RUMBLES
10
10
The Science Bank
10
10
10
10
TEN RUMBLES
10
10
The Science Bank
10
10
10
10
TEN RUMBLES
10
10
The Science Bank
10
10
10
10
TEN RUMBLES
10

50
The Science Bank
50
50
50
APPLE SAUCE
50
FIFTY RUMBLES
50
50
The Science Bank
50
50
50
APPLE SAUCE
50
FIFTY RUMBLES
50
20
The Science Bank
20
20
20
20
TWENTY RUMBLES
20
20
The Science Bank
20
20
20
20
TWENTY RUMBLES
20

Do it Again!

Part 1 - In one science investigation some pupils were finding out whether the height of drop made a difference to how high the ball bounced. In another, they were seeing how the distance between a puppet and a light source affected the height of the shadow. In which investigation would it be more important to take repeat readings? Why?

Part 2 - Imagine you are doing an investigation. You have to decide how many repeat readings to take. You want your results to be reliable but you don't want to waste time. What would you consider to help you decide how many repeat readings to do?

Part 3 - Look at the two tables below. They show results from two different groups working on the same investigation. Whose results would you trust more? Why?

GROUP 1

Angle of ramp (°)	How far can rolled (cm)				
	1st reading	2nd reading	3rd reading	4th reading	5th reading
10	19	21	20	20	21
20	28	28	27	28	27
30	40	39	39	40	39
40	55	56	55	54	55
50	57	58	57	59	57
60	42	42	42	41	42

GROUP 2

Angle of ramp (°)	How far can rolled (cm)				
	1st reading	2nd reading	3rd reading	4th reading	5th reading
10	19.6	24.1	18.1	19.2	26.8
20	26.2	29.0	31.3	33.6	25.5
30	44.1	36.3	45.3	37.0	39.8
40	56.0	66.4	58.3	61.3	58.5
50	60.0	64.3	56.4	58.0	53.4
60	44.6	48.2	39.9	41.7	42.5

Using Tables

Table Talk

Using Tables

Table Talk

WHAT IS IT?

The object of this game is for pupils to work out whether information provided in a table supports a particular statement. They are given a blank table with spaces for information about five mythical planets such as their diameter, gravity and temperature; all compared with those of Earth. The numbers are decided by chance using a die, called out by the teacher and filled in on the table by the pupils working in pairs. The pupils call out when they think that the table shows enough evidence to make a decision about their particular statement.

WHY IS IT IMPORTANT?

Tables are important organising tools in science. This game gives pupils practice in completing and interpreting the information shown in a table and also asks them to think about whether they have sufficient evidence to support or refute a statement.

- Pupils can get muddled about what the information in a table represents or just bewildered with the quantity of information to interpret.
- Pupils often draw conclusions too soon, without collecting all the necessary evidence. They need to develop the art of focusing on particular bits of information whilst not forgetting the rest.
- Pupils need to use formal scientific language to become familiar with it. In this game pupils have to call out one of the phrases "Evidence supports the statement" or "Evidence does not support the statement".

RESOURCES

Available in the book and on CD

BLANK TABLE (Version 1 and 2: one per pair/group of pupils)	P79
STATEMENTS (Version 1: one statement per pair of pupils)	P80-83
INCOMPLETE EVIDENCE CARDS (Version 1 and 2: teacher only)	P84-86

YOU WILL ALSO NEED

A die (or some other means of quickly and randomly generating the numbers 1 to 6)

Post-its (Version 2 only - different colour for each group)

2 pieces of paper headed 'supports statement' and 'does not support statement' (Version 2 only - a set per group)

How to play Table Talk

HERE ARE SOME DIFFERENT VERSIONS OF THE GAME

Version 1 - Whole class

- Give pairs of pupils a 'Blank table' (p79) and one 'Statement' (p80-83).
- Cut out and fold the 'Incomplete evidence cards' (p84-86). Put in a box.
- Pick out one 'Incomplete evidence card'. Roll the die. Read out the evidence using the number rolled e.g. "Vulcan has a diameter THREE times that of Earth".
- Pupils write the number on their 'Blank table' in the appropriate place.
- Continue, as above, to add more numbers to the pupils' tables. Allow some time for discussion.
- When a pair of pupils thinks they have enough evidence they call out either - "Evidence does" or "does not support, the statement".
- Decide, as a class, whether they had enough evidence to make the call.
- First pair to call correctly gets 5 points. The second pair 4 points and so on. Incorrect call loses 1 point.
- To encourage everyone to continue, tell them that they are all going to draw what life might be like on one of the planets to finish the game.

Version 2 - Groups

- Give groups a 'Blank table' (p79), two pieces of paper headed 'Supports statement' and 'Does not support statement' and Post-its.
- Roll a die until the blank table is filled, or give out a completed table.
- Give each group 5 or 10 minutes to generate statements based on the data, write each one on separate Post-its and sort onto the two pieces of paper.
- Groups swap papers. They give 1 point for each conclusion they think is correctly placed. Discuss any that are very interesting or where there is disagreement.

Version 3 - CD & Whiteboard

- Open the Blank Table on the CD. Play as in 1 or 2 above but add numbers on the whiteboard so that they are visible to everyone.

Extra Activity

At the end of this section (p87-88) you will find examples of investigations involving tables. Discuss these with the pupils, either to introduce the game or to review their understanding afterwards.

Table Talk (Version 1)

Background notes

Give pairs discussion time after each roll of the die. Insist that pupils call out either "Evidence supports the statement" or "Evidence does not support the statement" so that it becomes part of their everyday vocabulary. Once a pair has made the call, write their conclusion on a board. Ask others to say whether they agree or disagree with the call, giving reasons.

NOTES ON 'EXTRA ACTIVITY' INVESTIGATIONS (OPTIONAL)

To be used for discussion before or after the games.

INVESTIGATION 1 (p87)
Properties of Materials

The table shows the results of five different tests on the same seven different materials. Pupils need to interpret the table to decide whether or not the results support each statement. They can write their answers on another table, giving them more practice of using tables. The answers are shown in Table 1 below.

INVESTIGATION 2 (p88)
Hardness of Rocks

One way to try to find out the hardness of different rocks is to see which objects can scratch them. The table shows which objects scratched which rocks. Pupils need to interpret the table to decide whether or not the results support each statement. The answers are shown in Table 2 below.

TABLE 1

Statements	Evidence supports statement	Evidence does not support statement
All metals are attracted to magnets.		✔
All the metals we tested were good electrical conductors.	✔	
All plastics are transparent.		✔
None of the flexible things conducted electricity.		✔
All the materials that were good conductors of electricity were also good conductors of heat.	✔	
All metals are better conductors of heat than non-metals		✔

TABLE 2

Statements	Evidence supports statement	Evidence does not support statement
The clay was the softest. It was scratched by all of our objects.	✔	
The sandstone was harder than the chalk.	✔	
The granite was not as hard as the slate.		✔
A piece of chalk will scratch a piece of slate.		✔
Granite is harder than the other rocks.	✔	
The order of hardness for our five rocks, going from hardest to softest, is granite, slate, sandstone, chalk, clay.	✔	

Blank Table

You are scientists studying a far away star called Gamma Centauri. You have identified five planets which orbit the star and are gathering data about them. You have a blank evidence table and a statement. The data about each planet will be transmitted soon. You need to put this on your table. As soon as you have enough evidence to be sure about the statement, call out:

Evidence supports the statement.

OR

Evidence does not support the statement.

TABLE FOR DATA (COMPARISON WITH EARTH)					
Name	Diameter	Gravity	Air pressure	Temperature	Length of year
Vulcan					
Nimbus					
Minos					
Betazed					
Romulus					

Statements

Cut up and give one to each pair of pupils.

Easier

Vulcan has stronger gravity than any other planet.
Nimbus has a lower atmospheric pressure than Minos.
Betazed is hotter than Romulus.
Minos is the smallest planet.
Romulus has a longer day than Vulcan.

Nimbus and Betazed have the same gravity.
Minos has the same atmospheric pressure as Romulus.
Nimbus is hotter than one other planet.
Betazed has the longest year.

Statements

Harder

Cut up and give to pupils.

Vulcan and Nimbus have longer years between them than Minos and Romulus.
Betazed has stronger gravity than Romulus but weaker than Vulcan.
Minos is hotter than Nimbus but has a shorter year than Nimbus.
The biggest diameter planet has the strongest gravity.
The higher the temperature of a planet, the lower its atmospheric pressure.

Statements

Extension

The following sentences could be given out and used to promote discussion. None of them can be supported or refuted by the evidence for the reasons given.

Vulcan has the longest day.

(Evidence only about length of year not day.)

Big planets always have the most gravity.

(Even if supported by evidence, density, and therefore mass, may vary.)

There is no water on Romulus.

(Depends on temperature and atmospheric pressure but 'water' includes ice and steam/water vapour.)

None of the planets could support life as we know it.

(Likely unless a planet has all '1's ie like Earth. But 'life' isn't just human beings, bacteria, for example, might thrive.)

Incomplete Evidence Cards

Cut up, fold, and place in container.

Vulcan has a diameter ☐ times that of Earth.	Vulcan has gravity ☐ times as strong as that of Earth.
Vulcan has atmospheric pressure ☐ times that of Earth.	Vulcan has a temperature ☐ times that of Earth.
Vulcan has a year that is ☐ times as long as that of Earth.	Nimbus has a diameter ☐ times that of Earth.
Nimbus has gravity ☐ times as strong as that of Earth.	Nimbus has atmospheric pressure ☐ times that of Earth.

Nimbus has a temperature ☐ times that of Earth.	Nimbus has a year that is ☐ times as long as that of Earth.
Minos has a diameter ☐ times that of Earth.	Minos has gravity ☐ times as strong as that of Earth.
Minos has atmospheric pressure ☐ times that of Earth.	Minos has a temperature ☐ times that of Earth.
Minos has a year that is ☐ times as long as that of Earth.	Betazed has a diameter ☐ times that of Earth.
Betazed has gravity ☐ times as strong as that of Earth.	Betazed has atmospheric pressure ☐ times that of Earth.

Betazed has a temperature ☐ times that of Earth.	Betazed has a year that is ☐ times as long as that of Earth.
Romulus has a diameter ☐ times that of Earth.	Romulus has gravity ☐ times as strong as that of Earth.
Romulus has atmospheric pressure ☐ times that of Earth.	Romulus has a temperature ☐ times that of Earth.
Romulus has a year that is ☐ times as long as that of Earth.	

Properties of Materials

Some pupils tested different objects to see how they behaved and what they could be used for. They did five different tests. Here is their table.

Name of material	Test 1 Is it magnetic?	Test 2 Is it flexible?	Test 3 Is it transparent?	Test 4 Is it a good electrical conductor?	Test 5 Is it a good conductor of heat?
Wood	No	No	No	No	No
Steel	Yes	No	No	Yes	Yes
Aluminium	No	Yes	No	Yes	Yes
Brass	No	No	No	Yes	Yes
Polythene	No	Yes	Yes	No	No
Cotton	No	Yes	No	No	No
Acrylic	No	No	Yes	No	No

Here are some statements that the pupils made. Do the results in the table support their statements? Tick ONE box on each row.

Statement	Evidence supports statement	Evidence does not support statement
All metal things are attracted to magnets.		
All the metals we tested were good electrical conductors.		
All plastics are transparent.		
None of the flexible things conducted electricity.		
All the materials that were good conductors of electricity were also good conductors of heat.		
All metals are better conductors of heat than non-metals.		

Hardness of Rocks

Some pupils scratched 5 rocks with four different objects. Sometimes the object scratched the rock. Sometimes the object did not leave a mark on the rock.

Here is their table of results.

Rock	Was scratched by ...			
	plastic fork	matchstick	metal key	fingernail
Granite	X	X	X	X
Sandstone	✔	X	✔	X
Chalk	✔	✔	✔	X
Clay	✔	✔	✔	✔
Slate	X	X	✔	X

Here are some statements that the pupils made. Do the results in the table support their statements? Tick ONE box on each row.

Statement	Evidence supports statement	Evidence does not support statement
The clay was the softest. It was scratched by all of our objects.		
The sandstone was harder than the chalk.		
The granite was not as hard as the slate.		
A piece of chalk will scratch a piece of slate.		
Granite is harder than the other rocks.		
The order of hardness for our five rocks, going from hardest to softest, is granite, slate, sandstone, chalk, clay.		

Using Graphs

Build a Graph

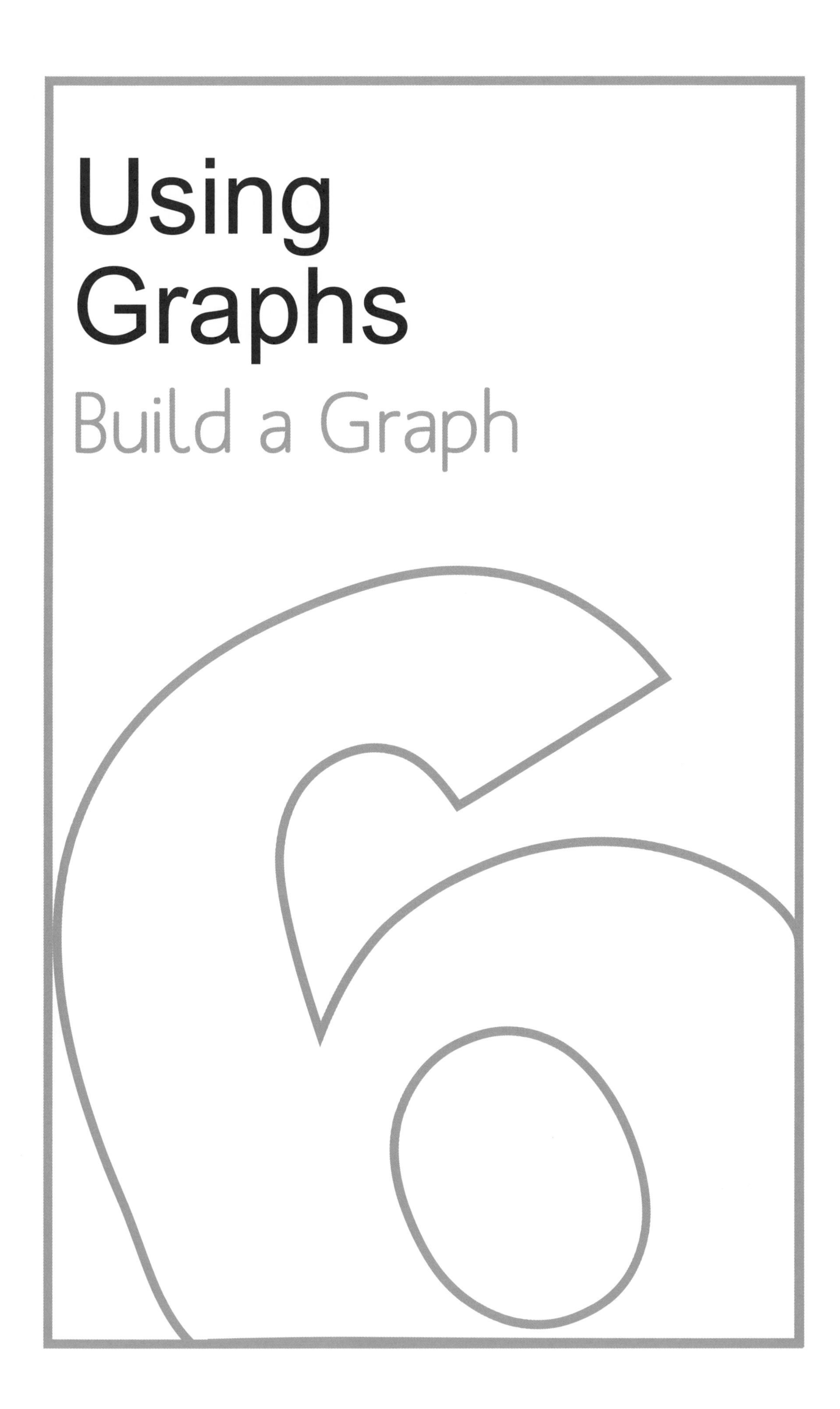

Using Graphs

Build a Graph

WHAT IS IT?

In this game, groups of pupils are given a table of results and they try to be the first to construct a graph that matches their results. Each group is also given an envelope containing a mixture of five different parts of graphs (2 axes, 2 labels for axes and 1 central part of graph with plotted points). Some of these graph parts could be relevant to their particular table of results and some will be to do with the data belonging to other groups. The pupils discuss which, if any, of the graph parts they need to keep and which to discard. They put those that they no longer want back in their envelope. At the teacher's command, they all pass their envelopes to the next table. The groups examine the contents again, keeping those parts they need and passing the envelope of discarded parts on to their neighbours. The process is repeated until one group completes their graph. There are 2 sets of tables and graph parts - one for younger pupils and one for older pupils.

WHY IS IT IMPORTANT?

This game enables pupils to see links between a table of results and the final line graph. Pupils also develop numeracy skills through discussion and by justifying decisions to each other.

- Pupils need to know how a graph is drawn up from a table of results and that in a fair test the variables written on the table headings become the labels for the axes.
- Pupils need practice in choosing scales and plotting points.
- Pupils should have opportunities to discuss patterns in graphs and how these relate to data.
- Pupils need opportunities to use the terminology linked to graphs.

RESOURCES

Available in the book and on CD.

TABLE OF RESULTS (Version 1: one table for each group. Version 2: selection of tables for each group)	P113 P114
GRAPH PARTS (Version 1: one mixed set for each group, Version 2: graph parts related to the tables given to each group)	P95-112
YOU WILL ALSO NEED *6 large envelopes to contain the graph parts. There are enough parts for 6 groups.*	

How to play Build a Graph

HERE ARE SOME DIFFERENT VERSIONS OF THE GAME

Version 1 - Whole class

- Print off and cut out all the 'Graph parts' (p95-112) (these can be printed from CD) and distribute them between the six envelopes, each one containing a random selection of 5 graph parts.
- Hand out a 'Table of results' (p113-114) to each of the 6 groups and explain that their task is to build a graph that goes with their set of results.
- Give each group an envelope.
- Ask them to tip out the contents and decide as a group whether there are any parts that go with their table.
- Those parts that they think go with their results are kept and put down on their table.
- Get each group to put in the envelope all the parts that they do not want.
- When all groups are ready, you give the command "Pass".
- Each group then passes on their envelope containing parts they have rejected to the next group.
- As before, each group selects those graph parts they want to keep and put back in the envelope all the graph parts that do not fit with their results.
- Pass on the envelopes as before until one group has built their complete graph.
- The first group to complete the task shouts out "Got the Graph."

Version 2 - Groups

- Give each group some 'Tables of results' (p113-114) and the graph parts that go with the tables. Muddle up the graph parts.
- Ask the pupils to sort out the mess and build a graph to go with each table.
- Vary the number of tables and graph parts used, in line with the previous experience of the pupils.

Build a Graph (Version 1)

Background notes

Copies of the completed graphs can be found on the CD. These can be used for your information, or shared with pupils after they have played the game.

The graph parts for the game are available on the following pages, Set 1 followed by Set 2. These will need to be cut out, mixed up, and put in separate envelopes for each group. They are also available on the CD.

Set 1
Graph Parts

Graphs

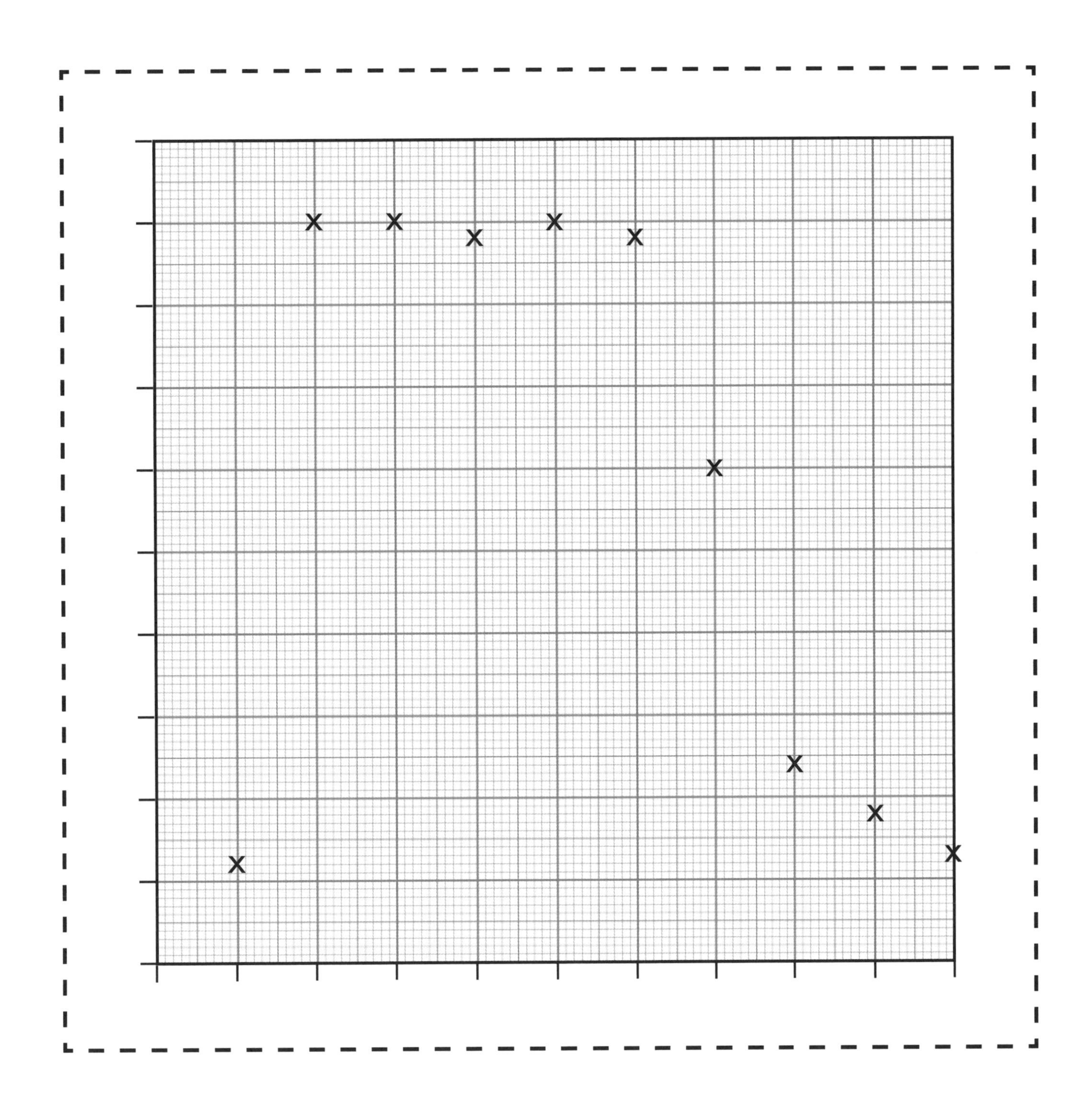

Set 1
Graph Parts

Graphs

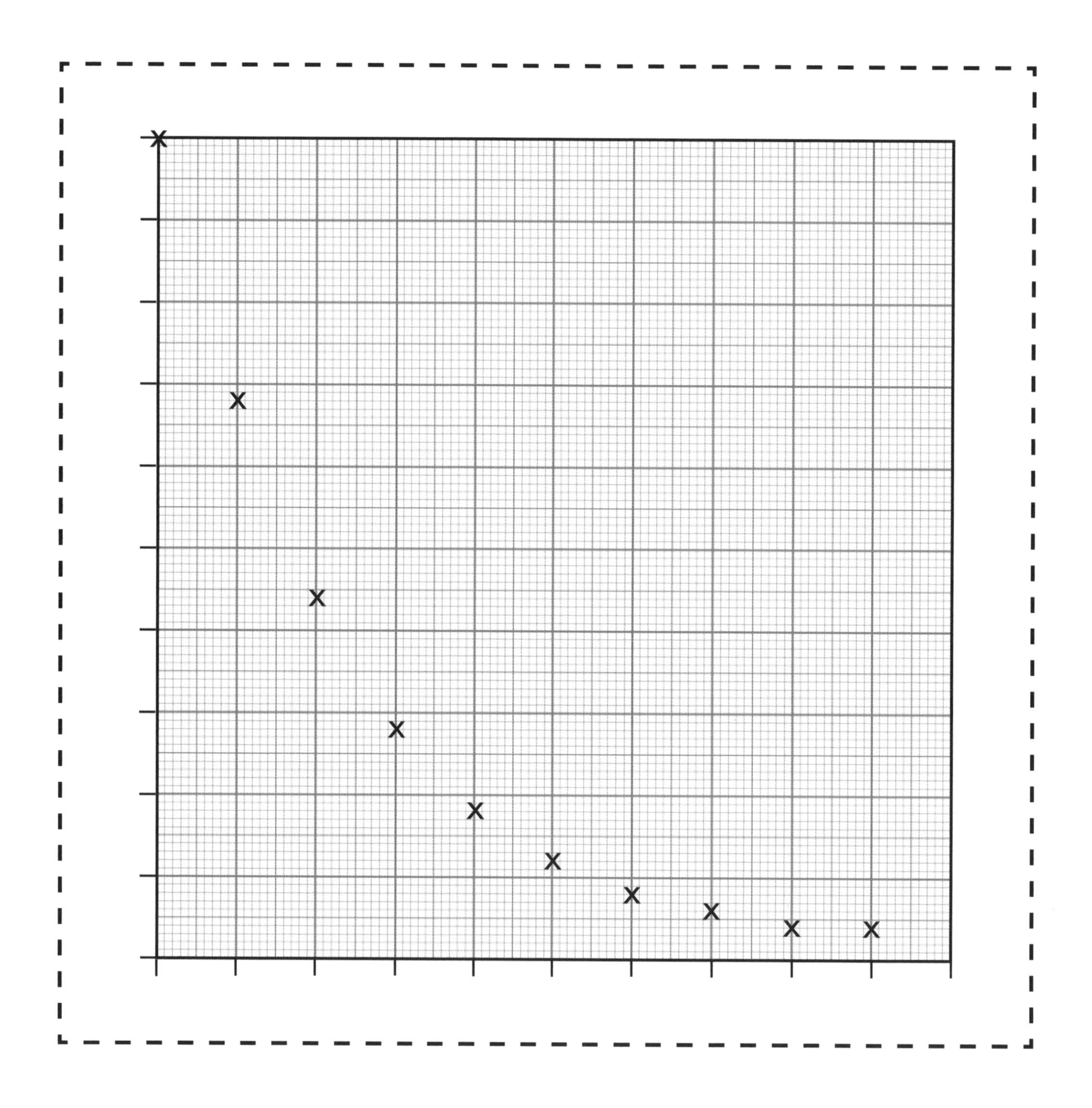

Set 1
Graph Parts

Graphs

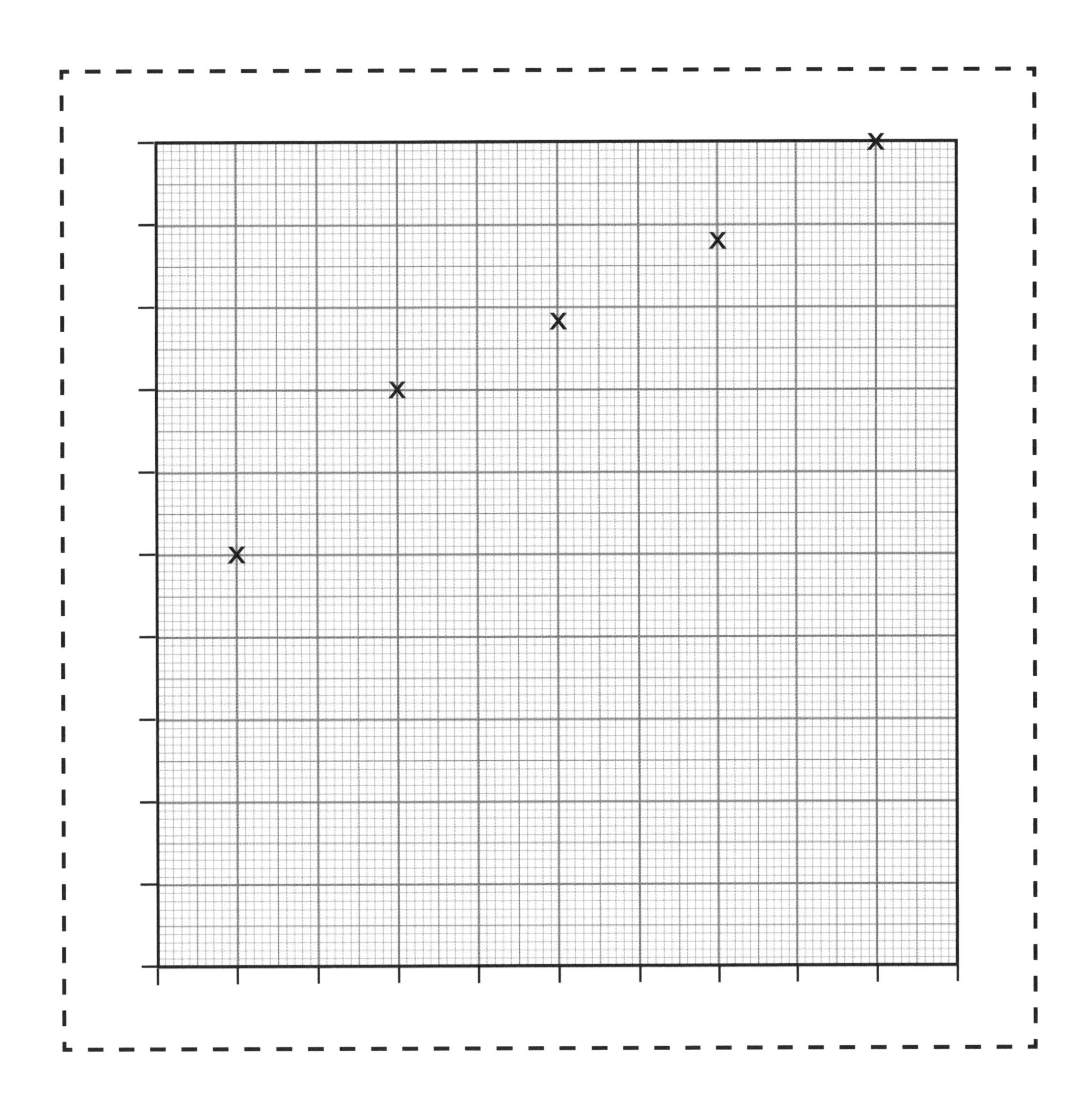

Set 1
Graph Parts

Graphs

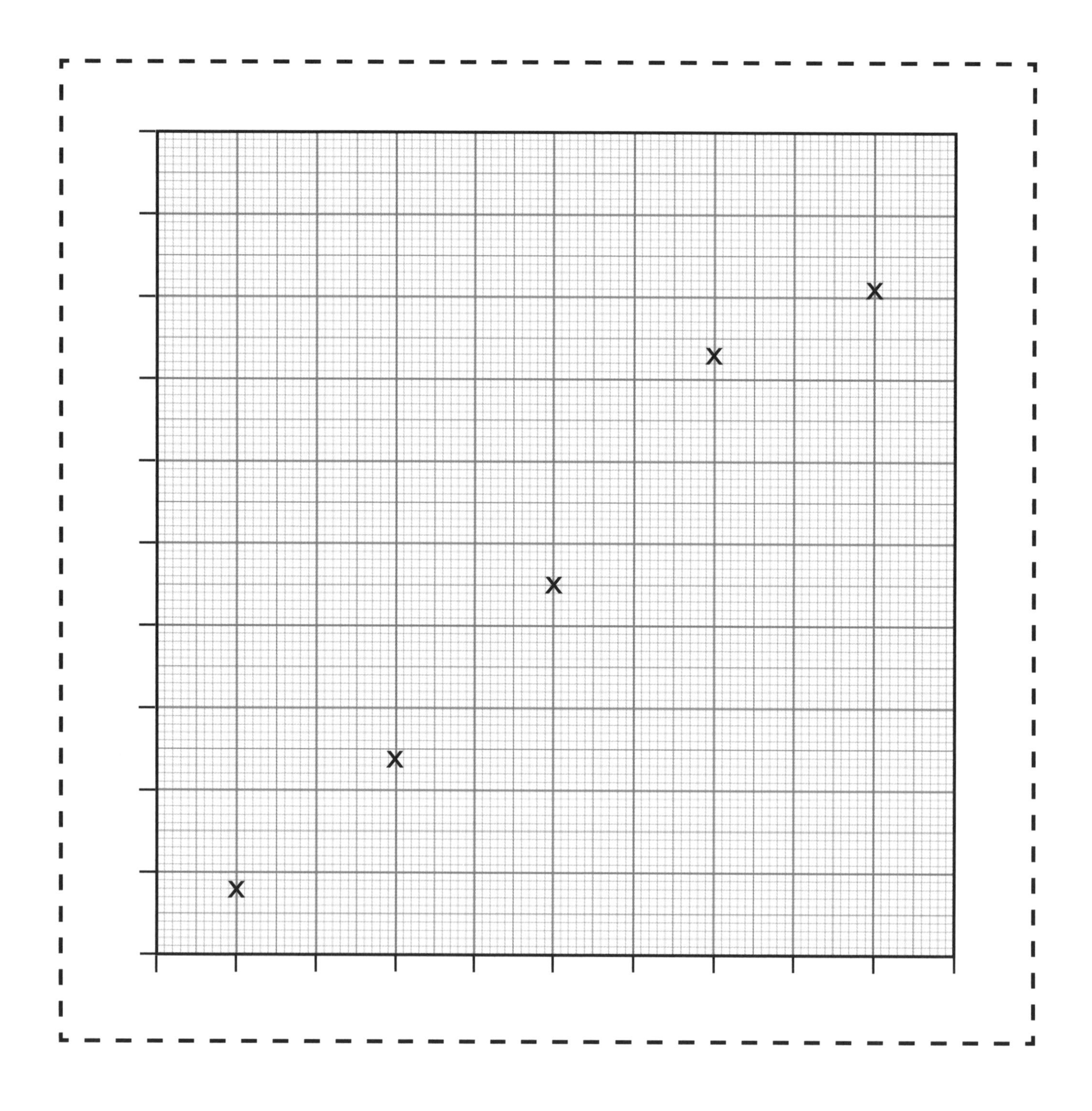

Set 1
Graph Parts

Graphs

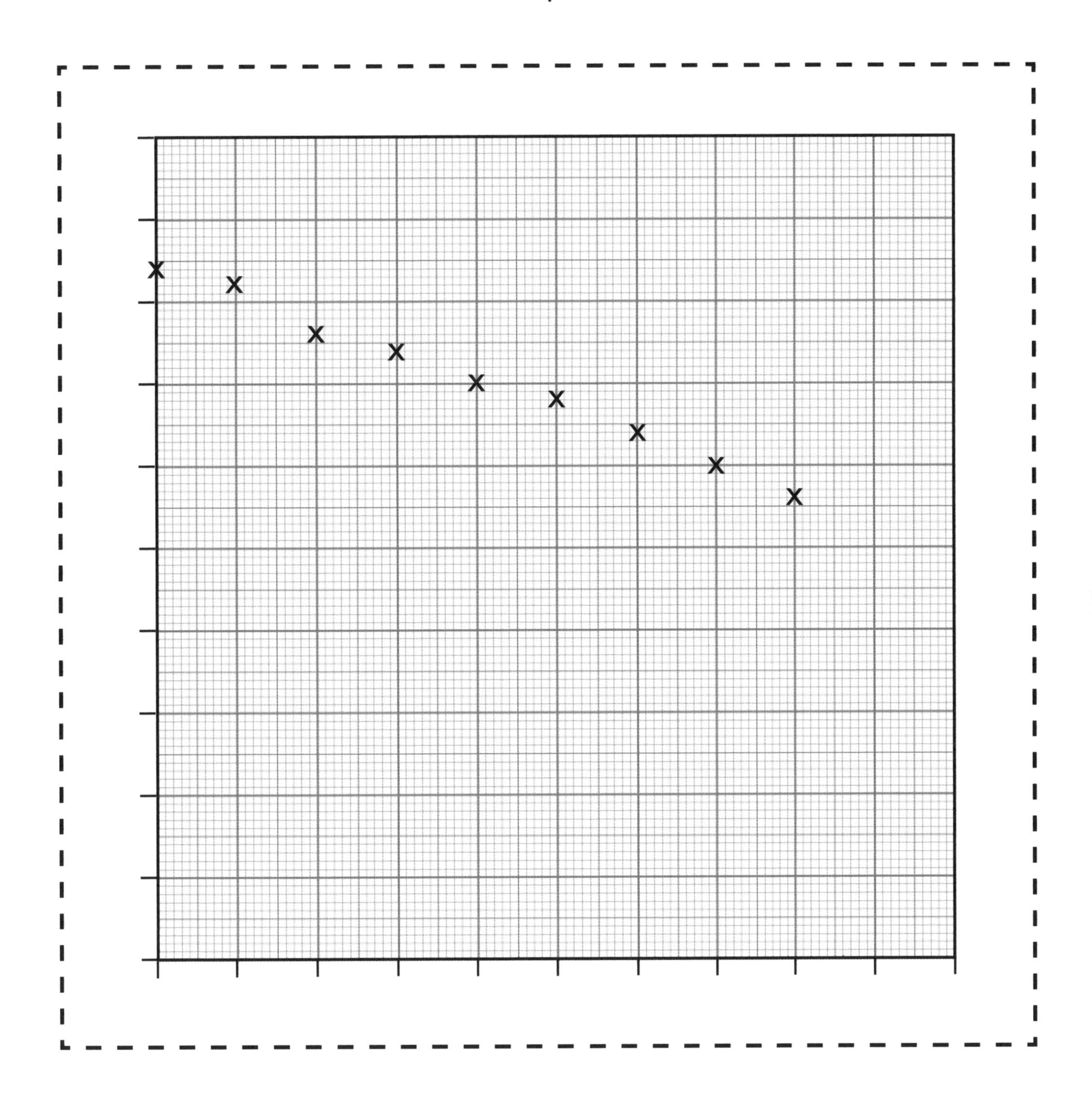

Set 1
Graph Parts

Graphs

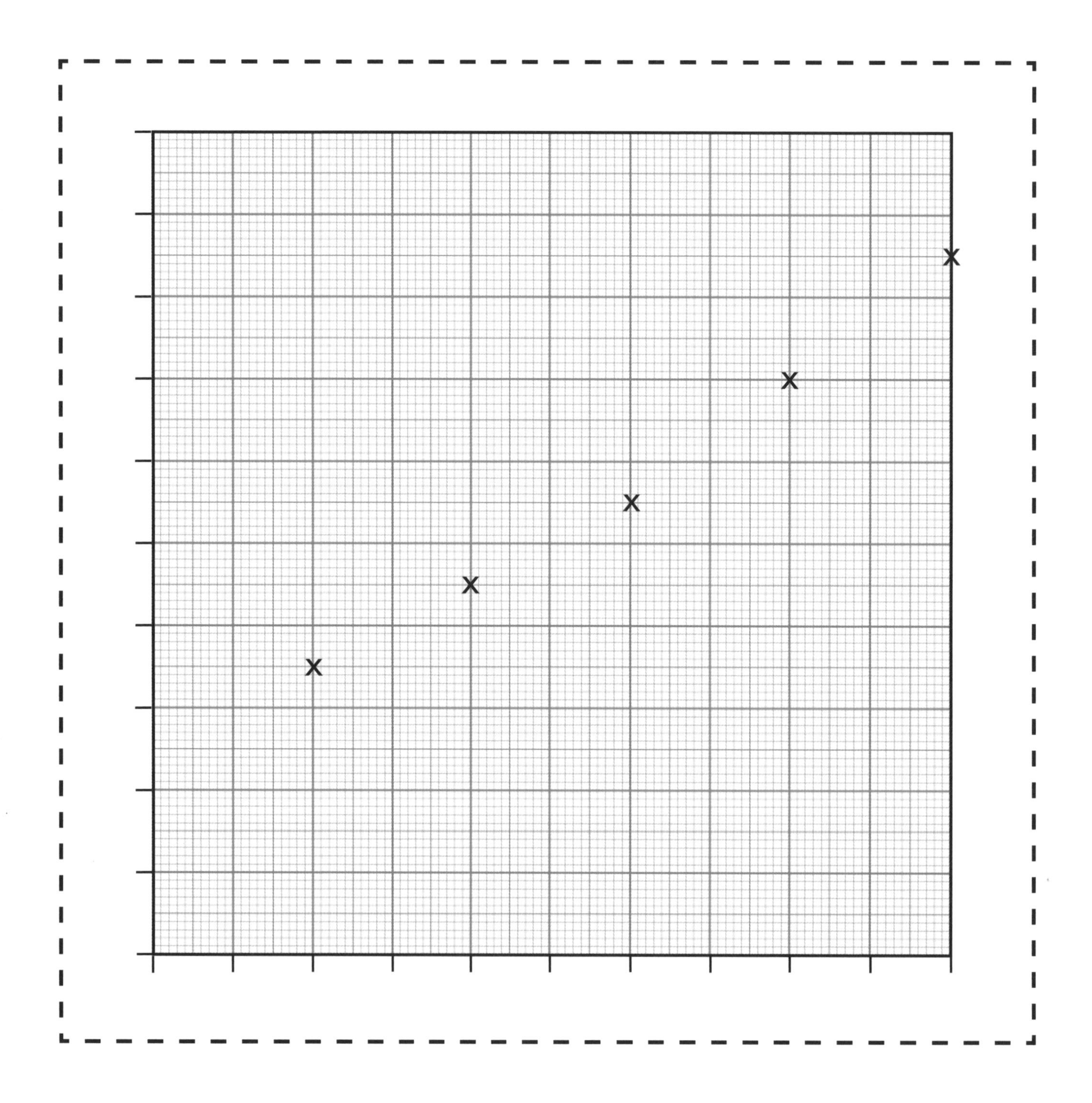

Set 1
Graph Parts

Vertical axes

170	70	5.0	100	50	20
160	65	4.5	90	45	18
150	60	4.0	80	40	16
140	55	3.5	70	35	14
130	50	3.0	60	30	12
120	45	2.5	50	25	10
110	40	2.0	40	20	8
100	35	1.5	30	15	6
90	30	1.0	20	10	4
80	25	0.5	10	5	2
70	20	0	0	0	0

Set 1
Graph Parts

Horizontal axes

Set 1
Graph Parts

Axis Lables

Time after start of exercise (min)
Pulse rate (beats per minute)
Time to fall 3 metres (sec)
Mass of burning candle (g)
Total length of elastic (cm)
Size of parachute canopy (cm^2)
Temperature of water (°C)
Time (min)
Mass added (g)
Height ball bounced (cm)
Time (min)
Height of drop (cm)

Set 2
Graph Parts

Graphs

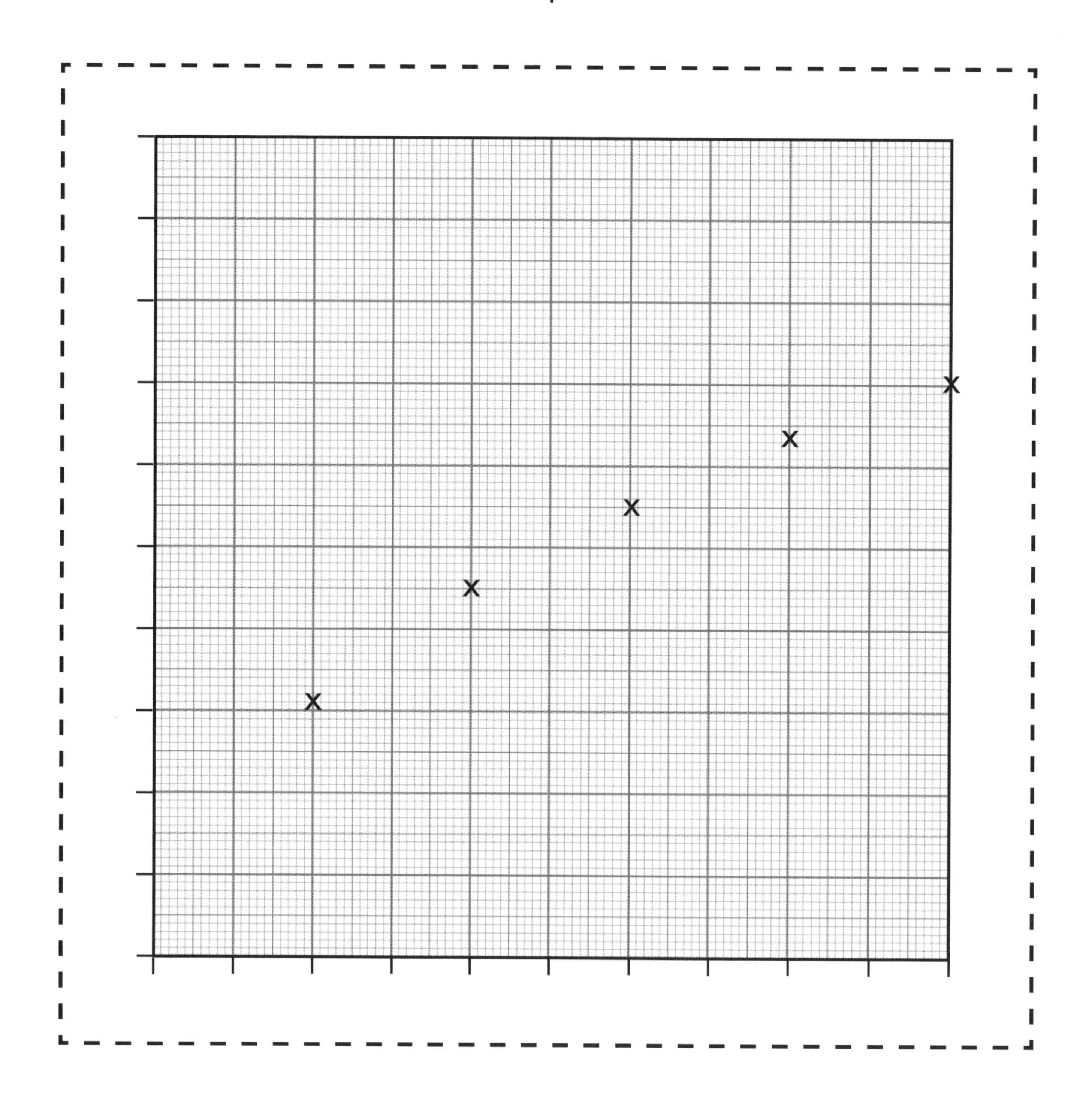

Set 2
Graph Parts

Graphs

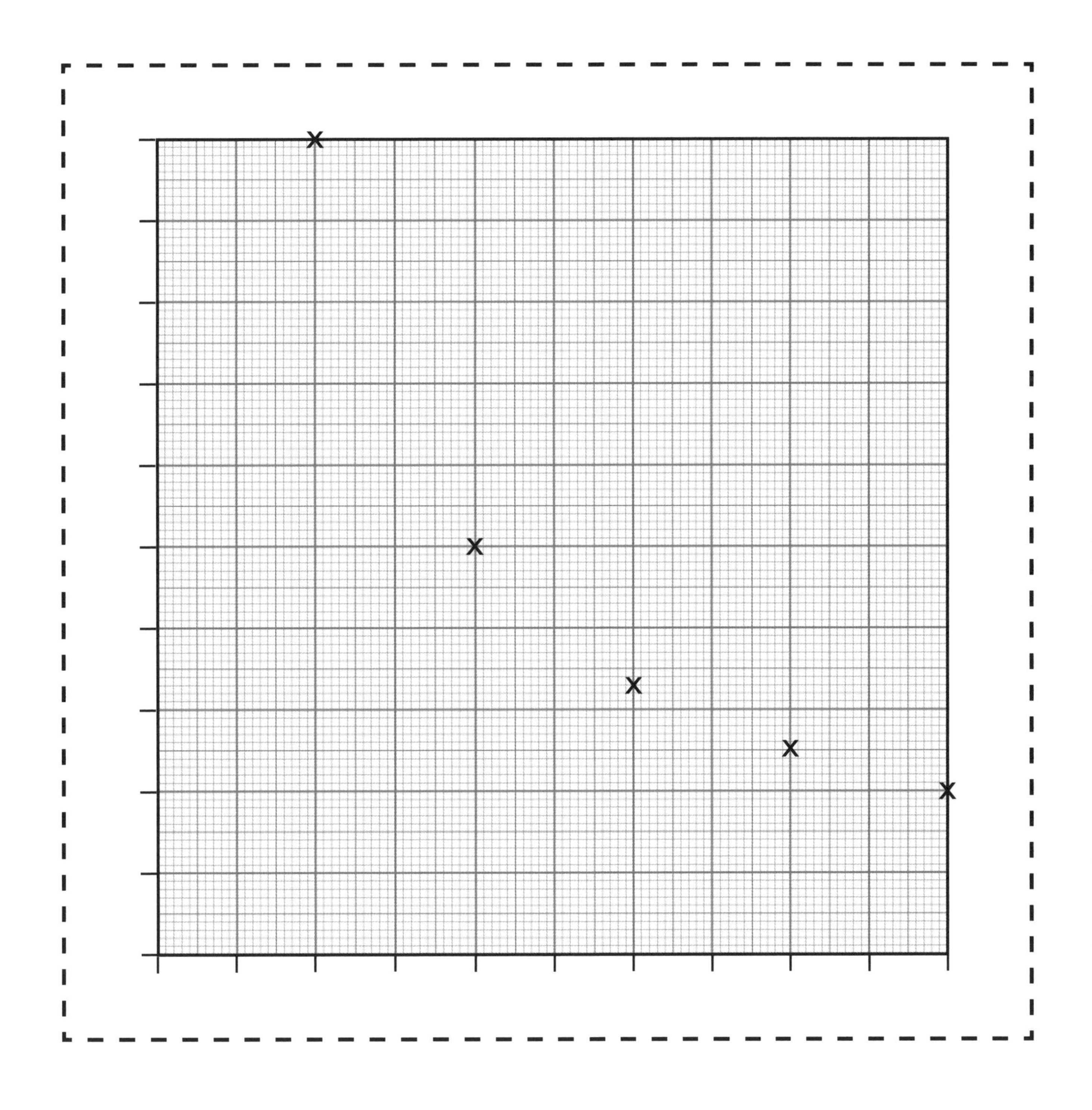

Set 2
Graph Parts

Graphs

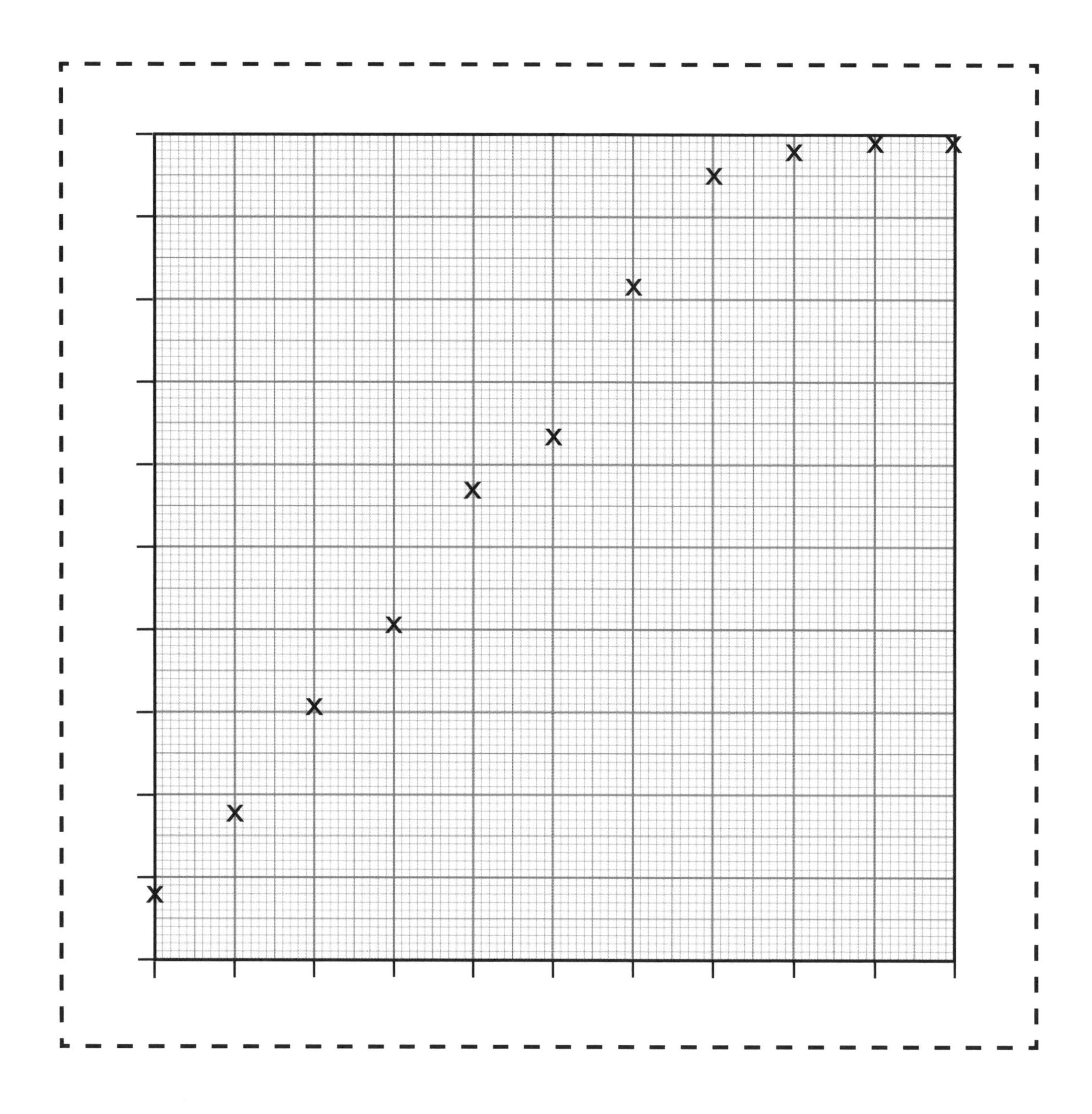

Set 2
Graph Parts

Graphs

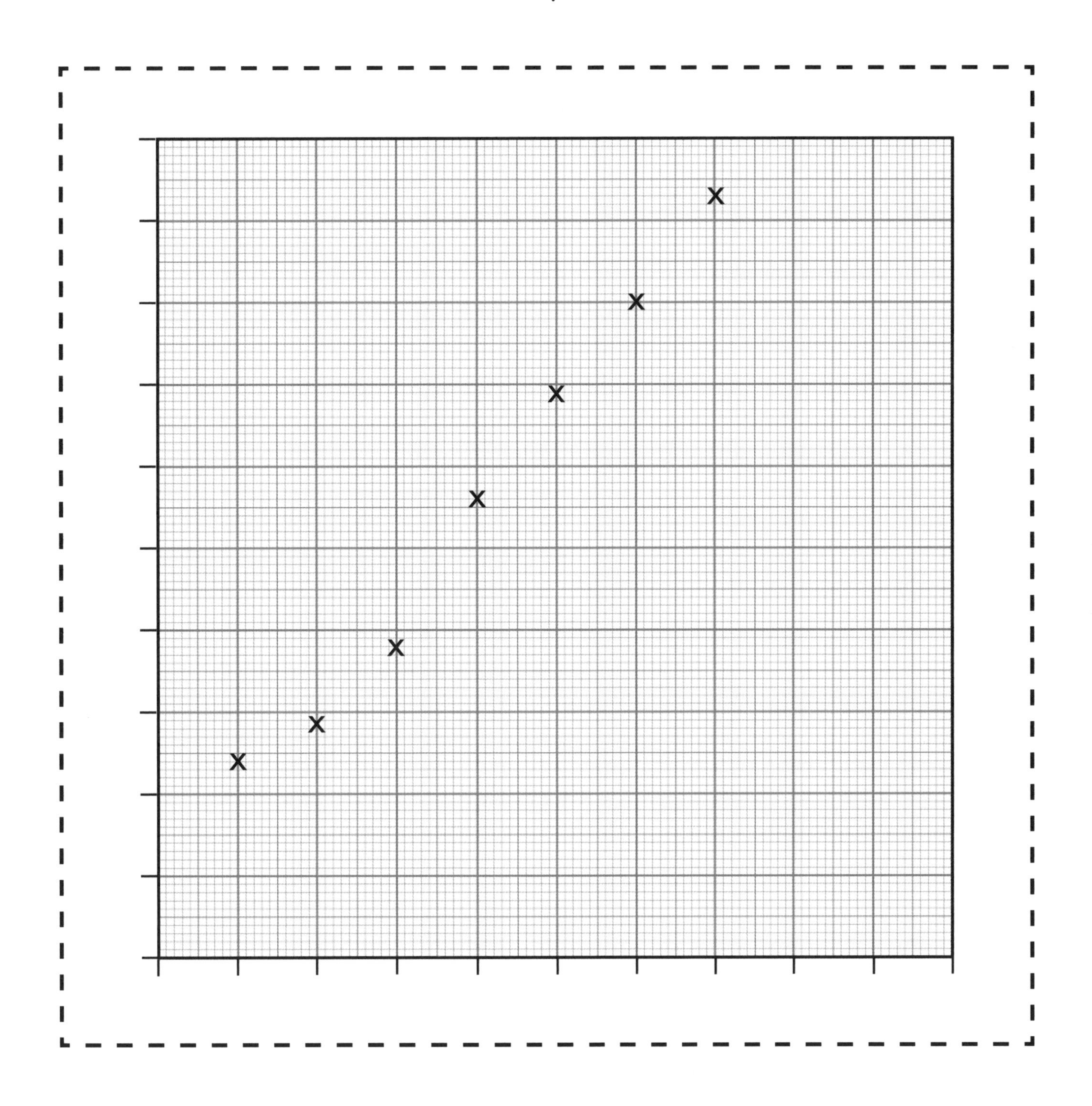

Set 2
Graph Parts

Graphs

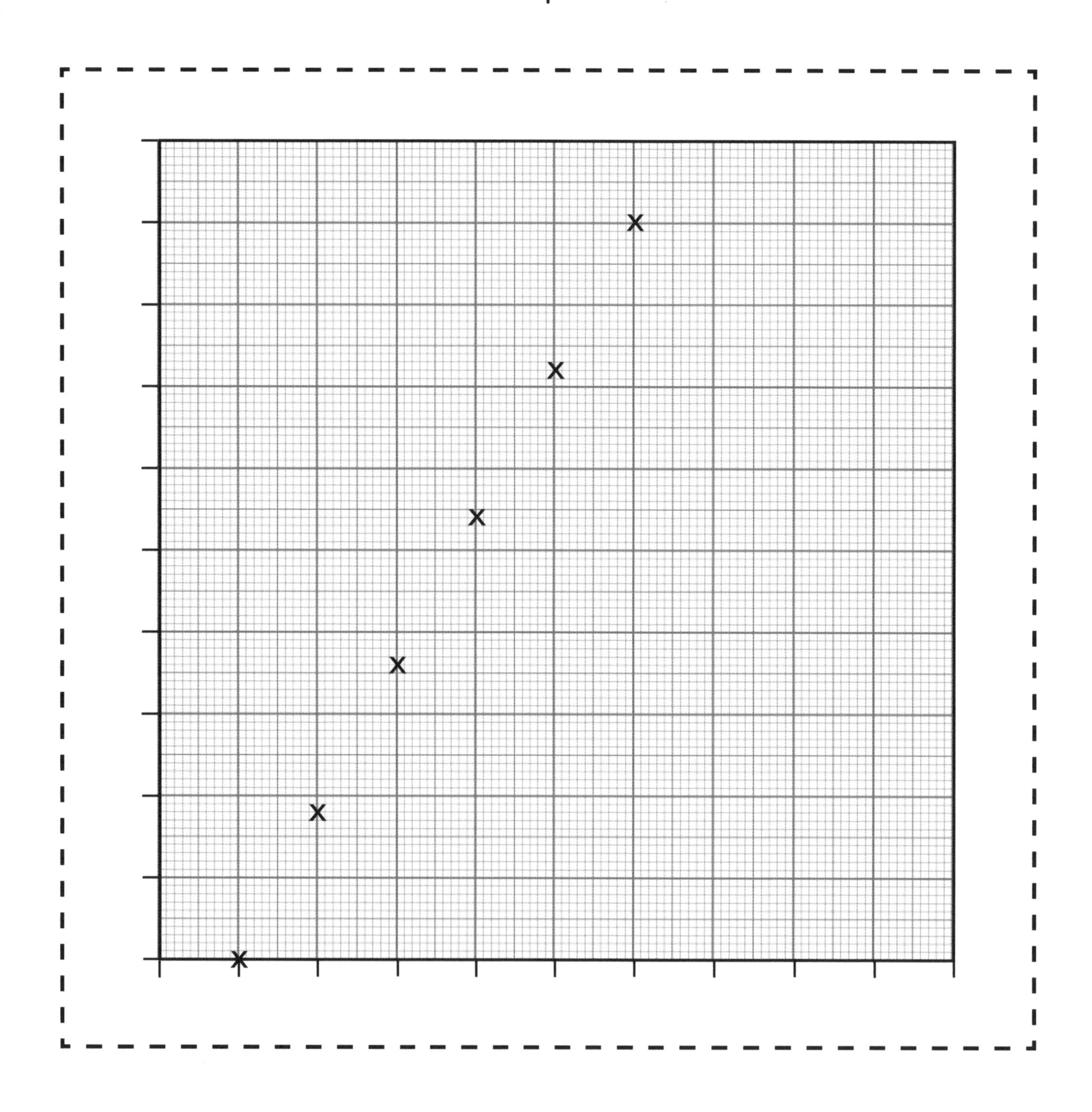

Set 2
Graph Parts

Graphs

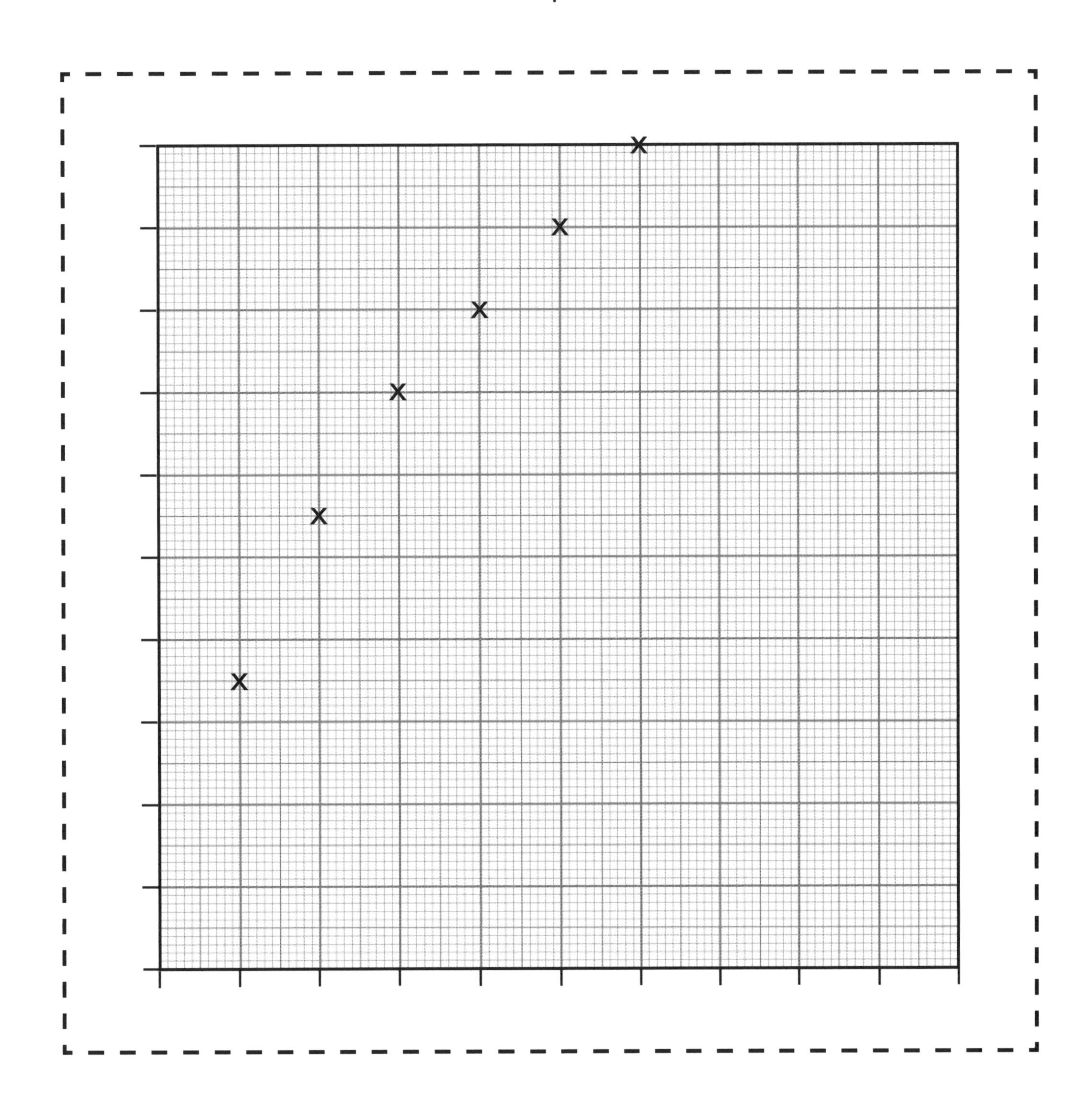

Set 2
Graph Parts

Vertical axes

20	1.0	2.50	50	5	20
18	0.9	2.25	45		18
16	0.8	2.00	40	4	16
14	0.7	1.75	35		14
12	0.6	1.50	30	3	12
10	0.5	1.25	25		10
8	0.4	1.00	20	2	8
6	0.3	0.75	15		6
4	0.2	0.50	10	1	4
2	0.1	0.25	5		2
0	0	0	0	0	0

Set 1
Graph Parts

Horizontal axes

Set 2
Graph Parts

Axis Lables

Temperature of gas (°C)
Length of pendulum (cm)
Mass of copper sulphate dissolved (g)
Mass added to block (g)
Length of wire (cm)
Current (amps)
Age (weeks)
Force needed to make it start to move (N)
Increase in volume of gas (cm^3)
Mass of kitten (kg)
Temperature of water (°C)
Time to do 10 swings (sec)

Set 1
Tables of Results

One per group

Time after start of exercise (min)	Pulse rate (beats per min)
1	82
2	160
3	160
4	158
5	160
6	158
7	130
8	94
9	88
10	83

Time (min)	Temperature of water (ºC)
0	70
2	54
4	42
6	34
8	29
10	26
12	24
14	23
16	22
18	22

Size of parachute canopy (cm^2)	Time to fall 3 metres (sec)
40	2.5
60	3.5
80	3.9
100	4.4
120	5.0

Height of drop (cm)	Height ball bounced (cm)
20	8
60	24
100	45
140	73
180	81

Time (min)	Mass of burning candle (g)
0	42
5	41
10	38
15	37
20	35
25	34
30	32
35	30
40	28

Mass added (g)	Total length of elastic (cm)
100	7
200	9
300	11
400	14
500	17

Set 2
Tables of Results

One per group

Length of pendulum (cm)	Time to do 10 swings (sec)
10	6.3
20	9.0
30	11.0
40	12.7
50	14.0

Length of wire (cm)	Current (amps)
20	1.00
40	0.50
60	0.33
80	0.25
100	0.20

Age (weeks)	Mass of kitten (kg)
0	0.21
4	0.45
8	0.76
12	1.01
16	1.42
20	1.56
24	2.03
28	2.34
32	2.46
36	2.48
40	2.48

Temperature of water (ºC)	Mass of copper sulphate dissolved (g)
10	12.2
20	14.8
30	19.3
40	28.0
50	34.7
60	40.0
70	47.0

Temperature of gas (ºC)	Increase in volume of gas (cm^3)
10	0
20	0.9
30	1.8
40	2.7
50	3.6
60	4.5

Mass added to block (g)	Force needed to make it start to move (N)
500	7
1000	11
1500	14
2000	16
2500	18
3000	20

Vocabulary

Vocabulary Bingo

Vocabulary

Vocabulary Bingo

7

WHAT IS IT?

This game is intended to reinforce understanding of scientific vocabulary in a fun way. Each group is given a 'Bingo card' containing a selection of words. The teacher reads out a definition, exemplification or description of one of the words. Each group decides if this matches one of their words and, if so, places a counter on it. The first group to correctly fill a complete row or column, and call out "Bingo", wins. The game can be continued with different rows or columns.

At the end of each game the group/s could be challenged to use one of the words from their winning row in a sentence. This helps to check that they're not just guessing. Only if the rest of the class, and the teacher, agree that they have used the word correctly can they claim their point.

WHY IS IT IMPORTANT?

Without a grasp of these key words and phrases, pupils will be not be able to take part in discussions about:

- their planning.
- the way they collect and present their evidence.
- what their results tell them.
- how much trust they have in their evidence.

Pupils need to know:

- terms they will meet when they carry out practical and investigative activities to be able to engage effectively in scientific processes and develop an appreciation of how science works.

RESOURCES Available in the book and on CD	
DESCRIPTION CARDS (Version 1 and 2: teacher only). (Version 3: one set per group to be cut up)	P122 P123
WORD LIST (Version 3 and 4: one set per group)	P124
BINGO CARDS (Version 1: one card per group)	P125-130
LARGE WORD CARDS ENLARGED TO A3 (Version 2: teacher only)	P131-137
YOU WILL ALSO NEED Counters (Version 1). Different coloured mini Post-its (Version 2).	

How to play Vocabulary Bingo

HERE ARE SOME DIFFERENT VERSIONS OF THE GAME

Version 1 - Whole class

- Give out a different 'Bingo card' (p125-130) and some counters to each group.
- Read out a 'Description' (p122-123). Give the groups time to agree if it describes one of their words and cover up the chosen word. Repeat.
- The group shouts "Bingo" when they complete a row or column. Let groups discuss definitions and decide if they agree. They can move counters after each round. Repeat.

Version 2 - Splat

- Stick the 'Word cards' (p131-137) on the walls. Give out different coloured mini Post-its to each group.
- Read out a 'Description' (p122-123). Put it where the pupils can see it. Give groups time to agree which word it describes. A runner for each group brings a Post-it and stands in the centre of the room.
- Now shout "Splat". The 'splatters' stick their Post-it to the word chosen by their group.
- Let the pupils compare their responses. Groups can change the position of their Post-it if they can justify the decision.

Version 3 - Matching Pairs 1

- Give out the cut up 'Description cards' (p122-123) and 'Word list' (p124) to each group.
- Call out a word and let pupils choose a statement. When you call "Match" one pupil from each group holds up the chosen statement.
- Repeat with other statements.

Version 4 - Matching Pairs 2

- Open 'Vocabulary Bingo' on the CD. Choose a description. Give groups a 'Word List' .
- Class to discuss and shout "Match" when they have chosen a word that goes with the description.
- Match the word to the description using a whiteboard pen. Have a class vote. If correct, award a point.
- Repeat with other descriptions.

Vocabulary Bingo (Version 1)

Background notes

1) The Bingo cards are divided into two groups depending on the words used. The first set of six include only the first 12 words in the list below, from 'observations' to 'discrete variable'. The second set, cards 7 to 12, may include any of the words listed. This should enable a degree of differentiation or use of the game by different age groups.

2) The table below gives statements for you to read out for each word. You could develop other alternative statements to match the words.

Descriptions (to be read out)	Word
Rashid said "The indicator paper changed colour from red to blue when I dipped it in the liquid". He was making an	observation
You can record the results of your investigation in one of these. It has words or numbers written in rows and columns.	table
You can display the results of your investigation using one of these when one of the variables is the name of a group or always a whole number.	bar chart
You can display the results of your investigation using one of these when both variables can have any value.	line graph
A line that goes along the bottom or up the side of a line graph or bar chart.	axis
If you change one variable and keep all other the same you are carrying out a	fair test
When you say what you found out from the evidence in an investigation you will be making your	conclusion
Something you change in a fair test in order to see what effect it has is known as the	independent variable
Something you measure in a fair test to find out the effect of the one thing you have changed is known as the	dependent variable
When something that you are going to change or measure can have any number value within a range it is known as a	continuous variable
When something you are going to change is described in words not numbers, (e.g. names of metals) it is known as	categoric variable
When something you are going to change or measure can only have a whole number it is known as	discrete variable

Descriptions (to be read out)	Word
Something which you keep fixed in order to be clearer about what your results mean is known as a	control variable
A measuring instrument with smaller scale divisions will give readings that have greater	precision
When you say why you think something occurred in an investigation you are suggesting an	explanation
You get this when you get relevant readings or observations from an investigation.	evidence
Jenny said "I think smaller pieces of marble will react more quickly with the acid". She was making a	prediction
Measurements that are closer to the true value have greater	accuracy
If you take measurements from an experiment where there is more than one independent variable your results will not have	validity
If taking measurements of the same thing several times gives you similar values then your measurements have good	reliability

Description Cards

Rashid said "The indicator paper changed colour from red to blue when I dipped it in the liquid". He was making an ....
You can record the results of your investigation in one of these. It has words or numbers written in rows and columns.
You can display the results of your investigation using one of these when one of the variables is the name of a group or always a whole number.
You can display the results of your investigation using one of these when both variables can have any value.
A line that goes along the bottom or up the side of a line graph or bar chart.
If you change one variable and keep all others the same you are carrying out a ....
When you say what you found out from the evidence in an investigation you will be making your ....
Something you change in a fair test in order to see what effect it has is known as the ....
Something you measure in a fair test to find out the effect of the one thing you have changed is known as the ....
When something that you are going to change or measure can have any number value within a range it is known as a ....

When something you are going to change is described in words, not numbers, (e.g. names of metals) it is known as ....
When something you are going to change or measure can only have a whole number it is known as a ....
Something which you keep fixed in order to be clearer about what your results mean is known as a ....
A measuring instrument with smaller scale divisions will give readings that have greater ....
When you say why you think something occurred in an investigation you are suggesting an ....
Jenny said "I think smaller pieces of marble will react more quickly with the acid". She was making a ....
You get this when you get relevant readings or observations from an investigation.
Measurements that are closer to the true value have greater ....
If you take measurements from an experiment where there is more than one independent variable your results will not have ....
If taking measurements of the same thing several times gives you similar values then your measurements have good ....

Word List

Words we use when we are investigating:

observation
table
bar chart
line graph
axis
fair test
conclusion
independent variable
dependent variable
continuous variable
categoric variable
discrete variable
control variable
precision
explanation
evidence
prediction
accuracy
validity
reliability

Bingo Card 1

Axis	Table	Discrete Variable
Line Graph	Observation	Fair Test
Conclusion	Independent Variable	Continuous Variable

Bingo Card 2

Bar Chart	Fair Test	Continuous Variable
Categoric Variable	Observation	Independent Variable
Axis	Conclusion	Table

Bingo Card 3

Table	Discrete Variable	Fair Test
Conclusion	Bar Chart	Line Graph
Dependent Variable	Categoric Variable	Independent Variable

Bingo Card 4

Bar Chart	Discrete Variable	Axis
Dependent Variable	Conclusion	Continuous Variable
Table	Observation	Line Graph

Bingo Card 5

Table	Categoric Variable	Observation
Fair Test	Line Graph	Axis
Independent Variable	Dependent Variable	Bar Chart

Bingo Card 6

Fair Test	Bar Chart	Discrete Variable
Observation	Continuous Variable	Dependent Variable
Conclusion	Table	Axis

Bingo Card 7

Observation	Categoric Variable	Precision
Axis	Line Graph	Validity
Independent Variable	Continuous Variable	Accuracy

Bingo Card 8

Bar Chart	Control Variable	Discrete Variable
Validity	Table	Fair Test
Conclusion	Reliability	Evidence

Bingo Card 9

Observation	Continuous Variable	Precision
Explanation	Line Graph	Validity
Conclusion	Evidence	Reliability

Bingo Card 10

Bar Chart	Categoric Variable	Discrete Variable
Validity	Table	Fair Test
Prediction	Accuracy	Axis

Bingo Card 11

Observation	Accuracy	Bar Chart
Fair Test	Categoric Variable	Validity
Dependent Variable	Evidence	Reliability

Bingo Card 12

Precision	Dependent Variable	Line Graph
Explanation	Prediction	Continuous Variable
Prediction	Accuracy	Axis

Large Word Cards

Cut up and display around the room.

Conclusion

Bar Chart

Validity

Large Word Cards

Cut up and display around the room.

Axis

Table

Observation

Large Word Cards

Cut up and display around the room.

Accuracy

Line Graph

Precision

Large Word Cards

Cut up and display around the room.

Fair Test

Explanation

Prediction

Large Word Cards

Cut up and display around the room.

Reliability

Evidence

Control Variable

Large Word Cards

Cut up and display around the room.

Continuous Variable
Independent Variable
Dependent Variable

Large Word Cards

Cut up and display around the room.

Categoric Variable

Discrete Variable

Working Safely

Safer Science

8

Working Safely

Safer Science

WHAT IS IT?

The object of this game is for pupils working in groups to decide how they can make a particular scientific enquiry as safe as possible. They are provided with completed 'Risk assessment sheets' on which the potential for injury/harm resulting from an activity and the likelihood of that occurring are each assessed on a 3 point scale. Pupils discuss how the risk might be reduced and by how much. Groups score according to the amount by which they can reduce the risk. If wished, Jokers (Hazard symbol cards) can be used and played once by each group to double their score.

Pupils need to be able to:

- assess risk and work safely, recognise hazard symbols and make simple suggestions to control risks.
- recognise the need for risk assessments and carry them out.

WHY IS IT IMPORTANT?

Practical scientific enquiry is accepted as a vital part of pupils' learning experience at all key stages. However, even simple experiments involve some risk. It is important that pupils learn to work safely yet see the magnitude of risks in perspective - the school laboratory is actually a 'very safe' place.

Making it as safe as possible does not need to make it less fun or less exciting. In science beyond school, like everything else humans do, an understanding of risk is important so that we can weigh up the risks and benefits for individuals and humanity.

RESOURCES

Available in the book and on CD

Resource	Page
RISK ASSESSMENT SHEETS 1-4 (Version 1: each group needs to have the same sheet)	P145-148
or	
BLANK RISK ASSESSMENT SHEET (Version 1: one sheet per group to use for other risk assessments of your choice)	P149
BID CARDS (Versions 1 and 2: one set per group)	P150
HAZARD SYMBOL JOKER CARDS (Versions 1 and 2: one set per group - optional)	P151 P152

How to play Safer Science

HERE ARE DIFFERENT VERSIONS OF THE GAME

Version 1 - Whole class

- Give each group the same completed 'Risk assessment sheet' (p145-148). Discuss the activity. It might help to show the equipment that is used.

- Explain that on the 'Risk assessment sheet' each part of the activity is judged according to the potential hazard.

  The numbers in the table show:

  How hazardous this action might be:

  1. Only minor injury/harm possible
  2. Could cause significant injury/harm
  3. Could cause serious injury/harm.

  How likely it is that an accident will happen:

  1. Very unlikely to happen
  2. Unlikely to happen
  3. Likely unless action is taken.

- The sum of the two numbers is a measure of the risk. A high score means a high risk and the activity should not be attempted. A low score does not mean that there is no risk but it is reduced.

- Explain that the aim of the game is to think about how the risk can be reduced. Talk with the pupils about what might be 'reasonable'. Maybe a risk of 3 is acceptable, but more than this is unacceptable. The more a group can reduce the risk the more points they score. See 'Background notes' (p144).

- Ask pupils to hold up a 'Bid card' (p150) to indicate by how much they think the risk can be reduced.

- Repeat for each part of the activity before any discussion takes place. When all groups have made their bids a spokesperson for each group explains their decision. At this point you may wish to allow or reject the bid, or allow class discussion and arbitrate if needed.

- Decide with the class whether the risk is now appropriate. (Possible 'answers' are given for the first activity (p141).

- You can give each group a set of hazard symbols as 'Jokers' (p151-152). They select the relevant one to play each round. The correct symbol allows the score to be doubled. For the wrong symbol, there are no extra points.

Version 2 - CD & Whiteboard

- Show the class a completed 'Risk assessment sheet' on the whiteboard.

- Ask groups what they would do to make an activity safer and how much this would reduce the risk. Award points according to the reduction if it is agreed that it is likely to have that impact.

- Allow other groups to 'trump' the group if they can suggest something that will reduce the risk further.

Safer Science (Version 1)

Background notes

The 'Risk assessment sheet 1' has accompanying notes below so you can work one through as a class. Another three 'Risk assessment sheets' are available, plus a blank sheet so that the game can be played with any current enquiry.

NOTES

Pupils might (for example) suggest the following:

Risk Assessment Sheet 1

HAZARD **Cutting wires of different lengths and baring the ends using a modelling knife.**		
Electrical wire cutters/strippers could be used instead of a knife. This might reduce the hazard to 1 and the chance that an accident will happen to 1.		
New Total 2	**Previous Total 5**	**'Bid' 3**
HAZARD **Connecting lengths of wire directly to a low voltage power supply.**		
Connecting a lamp and ammeter in series would prevent short pieces of wire tripping the power supply or the possibility of a burn on connection due to the high current. The hazard itself would still be 1 as things can still be incorrectly connected but the chance of an accident would be reduced to 1.		
New Total 2	**Previous Total 3**	**'Bid' 1**
HAZARD **Changing the current through the wire by switching the power supply.**		
Many minor accidents are caused by pupils turning the power supply up fully and causing the thin wire to overheat and the plastic insulation to melt. Using better insulated wire would reduce the risk, possibly to 1. The chance of this happening could be reduced to 2 by using a rheostat to vary the current or setting the voltage stop on the power pack. However, electromagnets require a high current so further reduction is unlikely.		
New Total 3	**Previous Total 5**	**'Bid' 2**
HAZARD **Using iron filings to test the strength of the electromagnet.**		
Using alternative small iron masses such as paper clips would reduce the hazard of eye damage to 1. Whatever is used, goggles would considerably reduce the chance of an accident also to 1.		
New Total 2	**Previous Total 5**	**'Bid' 3**

NB Pupils might suggest that the risk, or likelihood of an accident, can be reduced to zero by avoiding doing part of the activity or getting an adult to do something for them. Give credit for this idea, but tell them, for this game, activities should remain the same but a safer approach considered. You can also discuss with them whether zero risk is ever possible, or if some risk, or possibility of accident, is always present.

Health and Safety Risk Assessment

Sheet 1

TITLE OF ACTIVITY Investigating electromagnets								
What we are going to do Wrap insulated wire around rods of different materials. Vary the current and use iron filings to find out how strong the electromagnet is.								
DATE OF ASSESSMENT				CARRIED OUT BY				
HAZARDS Things that might be harmful	How hazardous might this be?			How likely is it that an accident will happen?			Total score	How could the risk be reduced and by how much?
	1	2	3	1	2	3		
Cutting wires of different lengths and baring the ends using a modelling knife.		X				X	5	
Connecting lengths of wire directly to a low voltage power supply.	X				X		3	
Changing the current through the wire by switching the power supply.		X				X	5	
Using iron filings to test the strength of the electromagnet.			X		X		5	

Health and Safety Risk Assessment

Sheet 2

TITLE OF ACTIVITY

How metals react with dilute acid

What we are going to do

Add small pieces of various metals to dilute acids in test tubes, watch what happens and test any gases produced.

DATE OF ASSESSMENT	CARRIED OUT BY

HAZARDS Things that might be harmful	How hazardous might this be?			How likely is it that an accident will happen?			Total score	How could the risk be reduced and by how much?
	1	2	3	1	2	3		
Cutting small strips of metal foil using scissors.		X			X		4	
Adding dilute acids to test tubes containing strips of metal by pouring from a bottle.		X				X	5	
Watching carefully what happens in the test tube.			X		X		5	
Using a burning splint to test the gases produced.		X			X		4	

Health and Safety Risk Assessment

Sheet 3

TITLE OF ACTIVITY

How much of an apple is water?

What we are going to do

Cut an apple into similar size pieces. Weigh them, put them into an oven to dry for different times and weigh again. Work out the amount of water lost.

DATE OF ASSESSMENT	CARRIED OUT BY

HAZARDS Things that might be harmful	How hazardous might this be? 1	2	3	How likely is it that an accident will happen? 1	2	3	Total score	How could the risk be reduced and by how much?
An apple is cut into 1 cm cubes using a sharp knife.		X				X	5	
Several pieces of apple are put into an oven. One is removed after five minutes, another after ten minutes and so on.		X			X		4	
The pieces of apple are put in a desiccator (glass container with a chemical which absorbs water from the atmosphere) to cool.	X				X		3	
When cool the pieces are weighed and tasted to check that they are still like apple.			X		X		5	

Health and Safety Risk Assessment

Sheet 4

TITLE OF ACTIVITY Growing bacteria								
What we are going to do Prepare agar plates (agar is a nutrient jelly that bacteria can grow on), add a small amount of 'broth' and observe the bacterial colonies that grow.								
DATE OF ASSESSMENT				CARRIED OUT BY				
HAZARDS Things that might be harmful	How hazardous might this be?			How likely is it that an accident will happen?			Total score	How could the risk be reduced and by how much?
	1	2	3	1	2	3		
Preparing (pouring) an agar plate so that it is not contaminated with bacteria.		X			X		4	
Inoculating an agar plate with a 'broth' containing known bacteria.			X		X		5	
Growing bacteria on the plate.		X			X		4	
Disposing of the plate and bacteria.			X		X		5	

Health and Safety Risk Assessment
Blank

TITLE OF ACTIVITY									
What we are going to do									
DATE OF ASSESSMENT					CARRIED OUT BY				
HAZARDS Things that might be harmful	How hazardous might this be?			How likely is it that an accident will happen?			Total score	How could the risk be reduced and by how much?	
	1	2	3	1	2	3			

Bid Cards

BID 1 CARD

BID 2 CARD

BID 3 CARD

BID 4 CARD

Joker Cards

Joker Cards

Evaluating Information

News or Views

Evaluating Information

WHAT IS IT?

In this game pupils are asked to read brief newspaper style articles, all of which have their basis in real media stories. They discuss them and decide which of several possible headlines might be supported by the science described. Each group has to agree whether a headline represents scientific 'News' (supported by evidence) or 'Views' (not supported by evidence). Discussion is a vital part of this activity. Groups are asked to explain their decisions about the headlines and even try to persuade other groups to support their view. Groups can gain credit by switching their view on a limited number of occasions.

WHY IS IT IMPORTANT?

Scientific enquiries are all about evidence-based science. Pupils learn how to obtain, analyse and evaluate empirical evidence. However, even if their evidence is good it is easy for pupils to jump to the wrong conclusions. Similarly in the media, reporting of science related issues can be faithful to the evidence or go way beyond it.

This game closely supports the 'How science works' aspect of the science curriculum. It encourages pupils to distinguish between the views that they and others may hold about science related issues and the conclusions which can be reasonably drawn from the evidence available.

Pupils need to learn how to:

- respond critically to news items.
- recognise the links between how scientific enquiries are carried out in school and the discussion of claims made on behalf of science outside the classroom.

RESOURCES

Available in the book and on CD

Resource	Page
NEWS CARDS AND HEADLINES (Version 1: one set per group)	P160-164
VOTING CARDS (All versions: one of each per group)	P165
SCORECARD (All versions: one per group)	P166
YOU WILL ALSO NEED REAL NEWS ITEMS (Version 2: one per group)	

How to play News or Views

HERE ARE SOME DIFFERENT VERSIONS OF THE GAME

Version 1 - Whole class

- Give a copy of the same 'News card' (p160-164) to each group. Allow a couple of minutes for reading and discussion.

- Give each group the set of related 'Headline cards' (p160-164). Allow time for groups to discuss the article and decide which headlines might be supported by the evidence. Explain that it is possible that none of the headlines represent scientific 'News'.

- Read out a headline. On your call, ask each group to call out "News" or "Views" and hold up a 'Voting card' (p165) showing this. Repeat this with each headline. Note decisions as they are revealed and emphasise that these cannot be changed at this point. Groups record their decisions on the 'Scorecard' (p166).

- Discuss the headlines and ask groups to explain why they voted as they did. (Hopefully a consensus will emerge but you may, eventually, need to provide a casting vote.) Before agreeing the final answer, but after discussion, give groups an opportunity to switch their vote (from 'News' to 'Views' or vice versa). Decide in advance whether each group can use their 'Switch voting card' (p165) just once or twice per session.

- Award points to each group for headlines where their vote matches what was finally agreed. For example, if it is decided that one specific headline is 'News' and the other three are 'Views' then a group who correctly decides this scores 4 points.

- Repeat with another article and headlines. If at the end of the game a 'tie breaker' is needed, give the groups an article and ask them to come up with one 'News' or 'Views' headline for the rest of the class to vote on as best.

Version 2 - Groups

- Give each group a real example of a media science report.

- Give them time to create their own 'News or Views' headlines.

- Play the game as above using the headlines from each group.

Version 3 - CD & Whiteboard

- Open the activity on the CD and share the 'News cards' and 'Headlines' via the whiteboard.

- Play the game as above.

News or Views (Version 1)

Background notes

The emphasis in this activity is on pupils discussing news items and how the scientific evidence they contain is represented in the headlines.

There are no absolute 'right answers' when it comes to deciding whether the headline represents News (N) or Views (V). However, the following thoughts may help guide discussion:

News Card 1		**Summer Weather**	
The chart shows how summer temperatures have varied over 20 years. There is substantial variation but the overall trend may be seen as upwards (based on data plotted every 5 years). However, picking different years may have given a different picture.			
HEADLINE 1 (V)	**HEADLINE 2 (N)**	**HEADLINE 3 (V)**	**HEADLINE 4 (V)**
It is not appropriate to predict from this evidence what will happen to the temperature next summer.	This headline rightly draws a distinction between weather which is highly variable in the short term and climate change which refers to long-term trends.	'It can only get hotter' suggests that the temperature will rise year on year (which the chart does not show) and that this is inevitable. Neither can be supported by the limited evidence given.	The article quotes 'a scientist' but science is about consensus so the focus should be on the weight of evidence not views expressed by an individual. The article does not provide any evidence to suggest that action may be too late.

News Card 2		**Brain Food**	
Although a local authority claims that the evidence supports the belief that fish oil improves brain power, the evidence given shows a smaller increase in exam results after fish oil was given.			
HEADLINE 1 (V)	**HEADLINE 2 (V)**	**HEADLINE 3 (V)**	**HEADLINE 4 (N)**
The evidence given does not support the 'official' claim.	This makes the point about tests needing to be long-term but no evidence is given by 'the scientists'.	The evidence is insufficient to make a claim either way.	This headline correctly makes the point that the evidence is very weak and does not represent an adequate trial.

News Card 3		Sunshine Vitamin	
The first paragraph reports a possible link between Vitamin D and a delay in the onset of certain diseases. The second makes connections between this vitamin and the effects of sunshine.			
HEADLINE 1 (V)	**HEADLINE 2 (N)**	**HEADLINE 3 (V)**	**HEADLINE 4 (N)**
Sunshine can have positive and negative effects on the human body. This headline focuses only on the possible positive effects.	This headline makes the tentative connection between chemicals produced by sunshine and health - the 'may' is vital.	Scientists may have found a possible link between vitamin D and certain diseases, but it is not their job to advise us to 'buy more pills'.	The headline correctly represents what seems to be conflicting advice. Although the article suggests that this is because the scientists are 'in the pay' of others, there is no evidence of this.

News Card 4		Smart Packaging	
The article outlines the technology of smart packaging and the views taken by different groups.			
HEADLINE 1 (V)	**HEADLINE 2 (V)**	**HEADLINE 3 (V)**	**HEADLINE 4 (N)**
Suggests that scientists are hiding something rather than just reporting what they have found out.	There is no suggestion in the article that the technology will be used before it is tested.	Raises the fears without any suggestion of benefit.	Is tentative ('could help') but perhaps one-sided.

News Card 5		Wine and Health	
This article revisits the old 'red wine is good for you' argument but supports it with some 'science' about antioxidants. It then makes a link between the longevity of those living in Mediterranean countries and their wine consumption.			
HEADLINE 1 (V)	**HEADLINE 2 (N)**	**HEADLINE 3 (V)**	**HEADLINE 4 (V)**
There is no evidence cited that suggests that drinking per se benefits health.	This headline acknowledges that there may be some benefit from red wine in moderation. The question mark is crucial as it suggests some uncertainty.	Although the article includes positive statements about antioxidants it relies on the 'knight in armour' picture and gives no evidence that they are cure-alls.	This takes the opposite view to headline 3 but suggests that there is genuine debate between scientists.

News Card 1

Summer Weather

The Daily Telitgraph

In spite of what seems to have been an awful summer scientists tell us that global warming is continuing to show in our weather. The temperature this August was similar to previous years and the trend is still upwards as the chart shows.

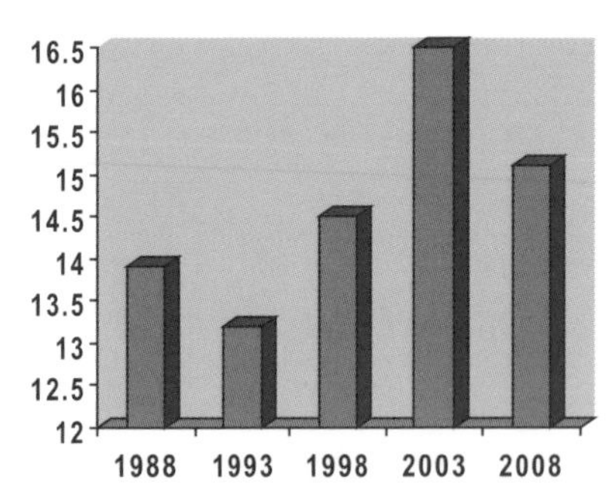

The cause of the wet summer is thought to be all the carbon that we are emitting from cars, industry and our homes. It is 'too late to stop global warming' says one scientist, so we must 'get used to bigger variations in our weather'. However, we must be due for a good summer next year.

News Card 1 - Headline 1

The trend continues - look out for a hot summer next year say scientists.

News Card 1 - Headline 2

Scientists give us the big picture on weather but the climate still seems to be changing.

News Card 1 - Headline 3

Global warming to the rescue - things can only get hotter!

News Card 1 - Headline 4

It's too late to stop global warming say scientists.

News Card 2

Brain Food

The Daily Mile

We have all heard that fish is good for the brain - just as carrots help us see in the dark and spinach makes you strong! But can fish oil actually help improve students' examination results? Well, one Local Authority tried to find out by providing 5000 children with fish oil capsules to supplement their diet and then seeing how their results compared with the expected performance. Examination results at GCSE rose by 3%, the previous year they rose by 5%. Those involved in the project said there was plenty of evidence to suggest that fish oil did improve brain power.

News Card 2 - Headline 1

Back to school - fish oil increases brain power - it's official.

News Card 2 - Headline 2

Long-term use of fish oil will improve results say scientists.

News Card 2 - Headline 3

Fishy story - oil makes no difference to brain power.

News Card 2 - Headline 4

Results don't pass the test on fish oil.

News Card 3
Sunshine Vitamin

The People's Paper

Scientists have discovered that the onset of some diseases may be delayed by taking additional vitamin D. This vitamin is produced naturally in the body by sunlight. The link with vitamin D may suggest why, for example, multiple sclerosis is more common in the more northern countries than elsewhere.

Scientists have been warning us against exposure to the Sun because of the risk of skin cancer. Now they say that sunlight is good for us. What should we believe?

Once again it is the rich people who can pay for expensive vitamin pills or afford to travel to warmer climates who will benefit. Can we really believe what the scientists say or are they all in the pay of drugs manufacturers and travel agents?

News Card 3 - Headline 1

Now the Sun is good for us - say scientists!

News Card 3 - Headline 2

The sunshine vitamin that may improve health.

News Card 3 - Headline 3

Shadow over scientists as they tell us to buy more pills.

News Card 3 - Headline 4

Conflicting advice from science - to tan or not to tan?

News Card 4

Smart Packaging

The Dependent

New developments in nanotechnology carried out at a microscopic level could lead to plastic packaging that stops food and drink spoiling by killing bacteria or preventing oxygen getting through the container. Scientists have suggested that these materials might also be used to enrich food with supplements and preserve vitamins that would otherwise be destroyed as food ages. Farmers could also use them to ensure the slow release of fertilisers at the right time for crops, and to detect threats from pests or pollutants.

However, the science and technology are so new that no-one really knows the effect this 'smart packaging' might have on human health, and environmental campaigners argue that we should stop developments now. Politicians, on the other hand, say that this technology has huge potential to help solve the world food crisis.

News Card 4 - Headline 1

More packaging pollution but scientists keep it under wraps.

News Card 4 - Headline 2

Smart packaging - but we are not smart if we use it.

News Card 4 - Headline 3

New threat from science -
this time it's the monster lunch (bag).

News Card 4 - Headline 4

New science of small particles could help solve big food crisis.

News Card 5
Wine and Health

The Daily Reporter

What is so special about wine? What is it that makes it potentially more protective against coronary heart disease, and perhaps other diseases, than other forms of alcohol?

Some scientists tell us that many human conditions such as heart disease, cancer and the aging process are caused or stimulated by a ravenous group of chemicals called free radicals that act like hungry sharks. They prowl the body and attack healthy cell membranes through a process that is called oxidation. Some foods, such as cranberries, are said to contain 'antioxidants' - chemicals that slow down or prevent oxidation. However, many scientists think that the increase in oxidation may be an effect of having the diseases rather than a cause. Clinical trials of antioxidants have been inconclusive.

Red wine in particular, we are told, is rich in antioxidants. So, drinking wine in moderation may really be good for us - as those who live in the vine growing countries of southern Europe have shown for a long time. Their life expectancy is known to be higher than ours.

News Card 5 - Headline 1

It's official - drinking is good for you.

News Card 5 - Headline 2

Take a little wine - for your heart's sake?

News Card 5 - Headline 3

The cure-all - antioxidants to the rescue.

News Card 5 - Headline 4

The fraud of antioxidants exposed.

Voting Cards

News

(Supported by evidence)

Views

(Not supported by evidence)

Switch

(We've changed our minds after listening to others)

Scorecard

News Story		Headline	What we think?	Class opinion	Score
1	Summer Weather	1			
		2			
		3			
		4			
2	Brain Food	1			
		2			
		3			
		4			
3	Sunshine Vitamin	1			
		2			
		3			
		4			
4	Smart Packaging	1			
		2			
		3			
		4			
5	Wine and Health	1			
		2			
		3			
		4